S0-AXJ-231

The Sound of Love

How Taiwanese Deaf Children Came Out of Silence Through a Touch of Extraordinary Grace

Written by Chi-Jun Hsieh

Translated and edited by
Margaret T. Bickley
Joy Nichols and
Cameron Duncan

The Sound of Love: How Taiwanese Deaf Children Came Out of Silence Through a Touch of Extraordinary Grace

Published in Taipei, Taiwan by Kenny Cheng

Illustrations and photos in this book are all from the personal collection of Kenny Cheng and the Children's Hearing Foundation.

Library of Congress Cataloging-in-Publication Data available upon request
Kenny Cheng
ISBN No. 978-957-41-4850-9

Book design and composition by Josh Talbot, USA, Type & Book Works Set in Arial

Printed in Taiwan

This is a love story that transcends culture, time, and language. A young woman born in California met a young man born in Taiwan, and together they created a fairy-tale family. Even though there were unexpected turns that came with the birth of their second daughter, they showed enormous love and care toward other families in the same situations. The paths of more than 2,000 families were changed for better, forever…

Joanna left behind the most selfless asset: The Children's Hearing Foundation. My great expectation for myself is to continue shining the light Joanna started, and reach for our mutual goal without ceasing, with her love and compassion. I also hope after you read this book, you can help us move forward by turning our thoughts into power. Let's make our mission a reality, in 20 years, to let all deaf children in Taiwan talk.

Kenny Cheng
President, Children's Hearing Foundation

The Children's Hearing Foundation and Chung-Yuan Christian University set up an auditory-verbal research center in the special education department on the university campus.

Joanna organized many activities for the Children's Hearing Foundation with love and passion.

Joanna warmly welcomed many Taiwanese and international visitors to the Children's Hearing Foundation.

Joanna gave many presentations to Rotary Clubs and often received donations to the Children's Hearing Foundation.

Joanna and Alana traveled the world together as depicted here with the two of them whispering a secret during a break at an A.G. Bell Conference in the USA.

Alana's older sister, Joy, played an important role in teaching Alana how to speak.

Alana received a bilateral cochlear implant in May 2007. Here Alana is photographed with Dr. Halit Sanli (EABR and intra-operative testing specialist) and Mr. Chris Rehn, Manager of SCIC (Sydney Cochlear Implant Center).

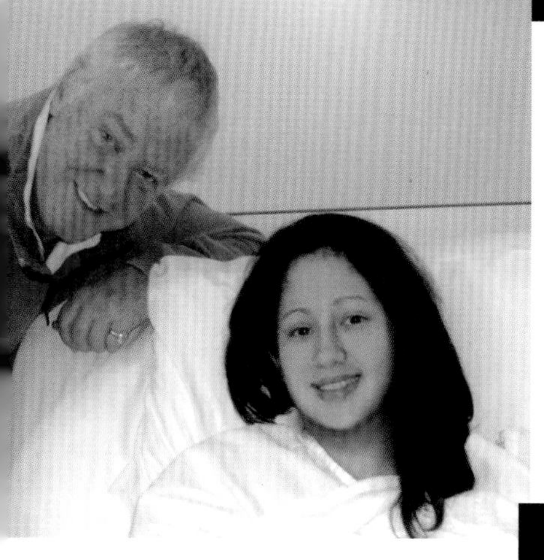

Alana is photographed with Professor William Gibson, ENT of SCIC. Prof. Gibson did Alana's bilateral cochlear implant in Sydney, Australia. Alana was the first recorded pediatric bilateral cochlear implant recipient with a common cavity malformation.

Alana and Kenny are photographed with Dr. Brian Pyman at a 2006 Cochlear celebration party. Dr. Brian Pyman was the ENT surgeon for Alana's first cochlear implant in 1993 at Royal Victorian Eye & Ear Hospital in Melbourne, Australia.

Alana, Kenny and Joy stayed in Sydney, Australia for two months after Alana received her second cochlear implant.

Alana is photographed with Dr. Jill Duncan. After Alana's bilateral cochlear implant, Dr. Duncan conducted intensive auditory-verbal therapy with Alana and her family.

Julie Ma, one of CHF audiologists, received her Master of Audiology in New Zealand, and additional advanced training in both Sydney and Melbourne, Australia. Julie and Alana are photographed in Sydney a few weeks after Alana's bilateral cochlear implant.

Alana was always happy and full of smiles in her mother's arms.

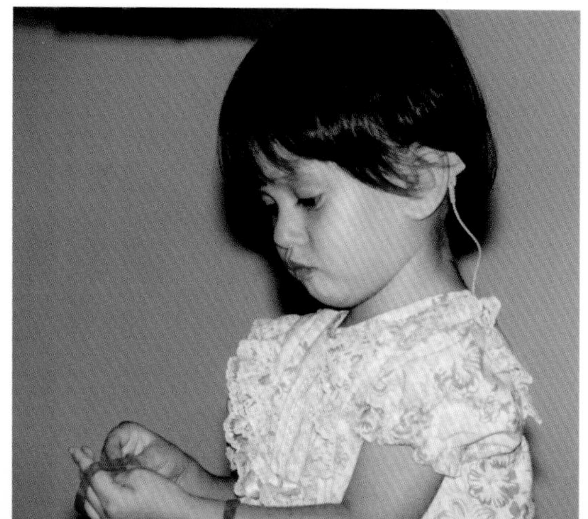

Alana was a bright, happy and curious child. Because of Alana's hearing impairment, well over 2,000 Taiwanese children with a hearing impairment have benefited from the work of CHF.

Kenny, Joy and Alana at the grand opening of the Joanna Nichols Memorial Library in the Taipei American School, where Joy and Alana studied.

Missing you Endlessly...

By Kenny Cheng

You have left us for a year...

Has it been a long year, or a short year? It's difficult for me to decide. I miss you so much that regardless of exact time, this past year seemed to have been the longest one of my life. However, committed to reach the goal we set together, I felt it was too short to accomplish everything.

24 years ago, you entered into my homeland from a distant country of your own, and with little delay, you quickly became accustomed to Taiwan culture. Destiny brought us together and backgrounds faded away and blended into one. Together, we built a successful business and a happy family, and we were blessed with a comfortable life. Everything was seemingly perfect, until we had our second daughter and found out that she was profoundly deaf in both ears, with little hope of ever speaking.

There is a popular idiom that goes, "When God closes a door, somewhere he opens a window." For us this was quite the contrary, God seemed to have opened a door for us, yet closed a window instead. Alana's hearing deficit forced us to face and endure a daunting trial in our lives. Through this perpetual and intricate ordeal, we never had the desire to give up. If put under similar circumstances, I believe that any parent who loved their child wholeheartedly would have done the same: fight to win back the life their child deserved, at any price. Throughout the process, you were so dedicated and relentless that the crisis was eventually transformed to victory. Through audito-

Chapter 1

"Daughter of Taiwan"

She seemed predestined for a life in the East, as though she was born with the orient in her blood.

Everywhere she went, a certain light seemed to surround her.

John and Mary had been waiting anxiously at the Children's Hearing Foundation for the arrival of its managing director. They had come as the parents of two hearing impaired children, with the same fears and concerns as all such parents. Would their children go through life without ever being able to hear the sound of laughter? Would they ever learn to speak?' They had never met the women they were to meet and whom they had sought out to answer those questions, though they had spoken to her over the telephone. She had gone by the name An-Ning Ni. The two had no reason to believe other than that this Ms. Ni was Taiwanese. They certainly could not have expected that she was the elegant foreigner who greeted them with a smile, Joanna Nichols.

Stepping into her office, Joanna sensed the helplessness of the young couple. Mary broke down as she related her anguish at her children's disability, and the suffering it had heaped upon her and her husband. Joanna could not help but share Mary's grief. She reassured her that, with commitment, and Joanna's guidance, Mary could teach her children to speak. Many deaf children, Joanna explained, came to the Foundation unable to say a single world. Before long, the same children would be greeting her with cries of 'Aunty Joanna'!

* * *

Joanna's first visit to Taiwan came in the winter of 1978. She arrived with a few personal belongings and a tremendous curiosity about the island. Though she was struck by the place, and the hospitality of its inhabitants, she could never have foreseen that it would become her home.

Joanna was a zealous adventurer and a natural traveler. She had a strong interest in foreign languages and cultures. Also, she was very much a people-person. She shared these predilections with her parents, Donald and Naomi. The Nichols ran an open-minded household, one not afraid of embracing the outside world. Donald spent most of his growing years in California, and took the profession of chiropractor at the age of forty. Naomi started learning ballet at three and was a ballet teacher for many years. Joanna and her sister Valerie were raised internationalists with passion for arts.

Joanna had a gift for languages. It formed the focus of her undergraduate years at Lewis & Clark College in Portland, Oregon. She majored in Spanish and studied at colleges in Costa Rica, the UK, and Spain. By the time of her graduation, she was fluent in not only Spanish and her native English but also Portuguese, French and Italian.

Mandarin was also a language to which Joanna had been exposed at college (coincidently in the lecture hall of a Taiwanese professor), but not one towards which she had, at that time at least, been particularly drawn to. Paradoxically, it was a trip to Paris with a mind to improving her French that fired Joanna's interest in Chinese. She had stayed with a Parisian Chinese-Vietnamese family. Needless to say, Joanna's grasp of Mandarin could only improve so much outside of a Chinese speaking country. It was for that reason plus her desire to learn chiropractice and acupuncture, that at the age of 24, she moved once more, this time to Taiwan.

On her arrival in Taiwan, Joanna wasted no time in immersing herself in her new environment, knowing that the only way to truly master any language is to understand the cultural and social context in which it is natively spoken. She befriended many Taiwanese, adopting their habits and mannerisms, and took a Chinese name: An-Ning Ni, which meant peace and tranquility. One of her Taiwanese friends suggested this name since the two traits seemed to represent the common impression of Joanna. Her dedication paid dividends: she achieved fluency in Mandarin in, by all accounts, an exceptionally short period. And speed had not come at the price of proficiency: Joanna spoke Mandarin, literally, like a Chinese, with a perfect Beijing accent, the equivalent of Queen's English. Not only that, she picked up a skill typical of a native speaker: she could distinguish between regional idiosyncrasies among Mandarin speakers. An impressive party trick, she could determine the dialect of a speaker a few moments into a conversation.

Joanna did not eschew the company of Westerners. She was a regular of Taipei's American Club in China, a major gathering place for expatriates, and was much admired by club staff for her courteousness and generosity. A senior receptionist recalled an occasion when Joanna heard that the staff were underpaid relative to the quality of the work they were doing, and volunteered to speak to their supervisor on the staff's behalf.

Though forthright, Joanna could also be very accommodating; which could be illustrated by this incidental fact about her life. She was a vegetarian. She adopted the preference under the influence of her parents, who disdained meat after having once witnessed the slaughter of beef cattle. She was well catered for in Taiwan, where vegetarians have, overall, more dietary options than in America. Yet, she was known for not imposing her vegetarianism on others. Whenever she knew there would be no vegetarian entrées at a meal, she would bring a kind of oat pastry stuffed with organic vegetables that she would make herself. If a buffet was served, she would eat whatever vegetarian food was offered, rather than asking for the preparation of special vegetarian meals.

Her body was as pure as it possibly could be because of her vegetarian diet, and consequently more sensitive. When she was young, she would feel sick at the smell of pesticide. She also rarely took any kind of medicine. The purity of her diet and physical being reflected the purity of her inner self. Joanna's friend, Dr. Sam Noordorf, described her as 'beautiful, inside and out', the way many of her friends and acquaintances felt about her.

* * *

Joanna was only enamored with Orientalism up to a point: she had an express antipathy towards Chinese men. The chauvinistic attitudes common among her male Taiwanese contemporaries ran contrary to her personal values and sense of self. Indeed, she was reputed to have once affirmed that she would 'never marry a Chinese guy'. Thus was her attitude when she first met Kenny Cheng.

To make a living, Joanna found a sales job at a textile importing company, Texma, in Taipei. In the course of her work there, on an otherwise unremarkable day, Joanna had an appointment at another company and met their sales representative, Mr. Cheng. Joanna would later quip that Kenny had come to buy her company's product, but had walked out with her instead. Medium-built, relatively thin and bespectacled, Kenny is not your average Taiwanese entrepreneur. His speech is precise and paced, free of verbal crutches or pauses. He is not flamboyant, as most elite businessmen; instead, he is contemplative and reserved, a model of solidity and steadiness. Kenny describes himself as a rationalist, saying he is so because of his engineering background.

What most impressed Kenny at that first encounter was Joanna's speech, her command of Chinese. When they first met, Kenny's impression of Joanna was of a lovely girl with outstanding linguistic abilities. She was committed to her job and spent very little money on herself. It seemed that she could live with few material possessions and yet still enjoy every minute of her life. Joanna, extremely embarrassed, had once to ask Kenny if he would lend her some money so she could visit her parents, who had moved to Australia. It later became a joke between the couple, as Kenny would say that Joanna paid back the loan by agreeing to marry him.

Intercultural marriages were then, even more so than now, beset by tribulation. Kenny and Joanna's was no exception. Kenny's family had been less than pleased when his sister had married a mainlander. Imagine then the rancor that an engagement to a westerner, and of all westerners an American, would have provoked. However, Kenny, shrewd as ever, knew his family well. The first time he brought her home to meet his parents, he introduced Joanna as his Spanish teacher. Sons who think they can outwit their mothers court trouble, and Kenny's mom was not one to be so easily deceived. She warned Joanna in private against marrying her son, and would complain to Kenny over and again that Western women were egotists, careerists and philanderers, prone to abandoning their husband and children. Certainly not marriage material. Kenny figures that the only source of his mother's edification on the subject was American daytime television.

Joanna's parents were not too enthused by the prospect of the union either. Joanna's father constantly put the point to his daughter that, as far as he could see, life for the wives of Chinese husbands was one of domestic oppression. Nevertheless, willing as always to keep an open mind about such matters, Donald and Naomi decided to see for themselves why their daughter was so committed to this particular man. As it happened, Donald's first meeting with Kenny involved a series of games of chess. The first round, Kenny marshaled all the wit at his command, and won. Donald signaled his approval with a nod and commented on Kenny's evident intelligence. The second round, Kenny, true to form, let Donald win on purpose. Donald looked at him and said with another nod and a smile: "You're even smarter than I imagined." Kenny's mother too eventually came around to Joanna. It was she that first suggested marriage. Few who met Joanna failed to succumb to her warmth and charm. With thoughtfulness and sincerity, the couple won approval from both their parents. Their wedding picture still hangs in Kenny's office. It shows Joanna radiant and resplendent in white. Whenever Kenny looks at the picture, his smile betrays his continuing love for her.

* * *

After they got married, Kenny decided to start his own business, Wonderland Nurserygoods, Inc., manufacturing nursery products, such as strollers, high chairs, car seats and the like, for foreign companies. The start-up period was tough: the suppliers he had known for years failed to honor the trust Kenny had earned through his dealings with them and required up-front payments prior to shipment. The firms he targeted as potential customers were also initially skeptical of the wisdom in contracting the new company. The money borrowed to start the business was thus quickly exhausted. Kenny saw both the worst and the best in human nature during that period, and it was Joanna's complete trust and help that kept him going. Wonderland is the sum of their hard work.

Kenny handled almost everything in the company. He was the CEO and the secretary. Meanwhile, Joanna worked in the factory in Wu-Gu (it was later moved to Tao-Yuan) from nine to five, and typed business letters to develop a global customer base from home at night. Her talent in multiple languages made it easy for her to develop international sales and win over several long-term buyers. On one occasion, Kenny and Joanna went to Germany for a business trip. Joanna didn't have time to hire a tutor to teach her German before the trip, so she listened to tutorial tapes during her spare time. Upon her arrival, Joanna could not only communicate effectively in German, she even ordered food for a dozen people at one of her restaurant engagements. It was truly amazing to witness! Kenny asked Joanna out of curiosity how she could learn German so quickly, with all its grammatical rules? Joanna answered breezily: she found the rules interesting, which made committing them to memory almost facile.

Joanna and Kenny had two daughters, Joy and Alana. Joanna passed onto Joy not only her beauty, but also her musical talent. Joanna had her childhood grand piano shipped to Taiwan from California. Together, she and her daughter could play the instrument with grace befitting its elegance. The two performed duets as though they were conversing.

Joy is reputed to have always been more mature and sensitive as compared with her peers. She feels as though she grew up overnight at the age of three, when her sister Alana was born. She explains that her mother became more occupied at that time dealing with Alana's hearing impairment.

Alana is more of a tomboy, according to her sister. She is outgoing and active, could always be found lingering around Joanna. Among the many roles Joanna played in her life, she put that of mother first. Joanna's life was extraordinary for being filled with ordinary blessings. A loving husband and two precious girls made her life complete. However, it was not without its hardships.

Chapter 2

Climb Over the Mountains into the Mist

It was the worst pain Joanna had ever experienced, but it would not beat her. She would fight it, defeat it, and see to it that her daughter led a happy, healthy life.

An airplane slices through the night sky above Taiwan. Bound for Canada, onboard a girl sleeps. Her cherubic face bestows upon her a celestial quality in the eyes of the woman sitting beside her, her mother Joanna. Joanna is envious of her daughter's tranquility. She lies awake, restless, meditating on her Alana's condition.

'There are moments in life when even Schubert has nothing to say to us', said Henry James. It is a sentiment with which Joanna would have concurred. She faced every challenge confidently and courageously, but had her share of encounters with the ineffable. On October 10, 1991, her second daughter Alana was born. The whole family adored this beautiful baby, but Alana was, to all appearances, not much impressed by their enthusiasm. With her linguistic talents, Joanna's hearing was doubtless sharp, and as such, it came as a shock to all when it was discovered that Alana was deaf.

Alana's hearing loss was classified as profound, the highest category and once known in the vernacular as stone deafness. So deaf was she, you could have placed the infant next to a pounding jackhammer and provoked not so much as a blink. Never had fortune dealt such a blow to Joanna, but she refused to surrender to it. Iron-willed, she resolved her daughter would lead a happy, healthy life, no matter the cost. Because, when it comes to their children, the slimmest hope is as manna from heaven to a mother. Joanna entertained the suspicion that a second opinion would deliver a different diagnosis. She was an optimist by disposition, never one to take bad news lying down. However, professional reappraisal, including a visit to the renowned House Ear Clinic in California, only reinforced the original doctor's findings. Alana was fitted with hearing aids, and a tutor, an Australian Catholic nun, was hired for her. A year passed with little improvement in her condition.

Kenny and Joanna were well connected within the international business community, and they exploited their network to gather information on what might be done for their daughter. Joanna involved herself in international medical organizations, their symposia and conferences. One such was the Alexander Graham Bell Association for the Deaf and Hard of Hearing. Bell is famous as the inventor of the telephone. The invention was, for lack of a better word, accidental. The original intent behind Bell's research had been to develop a sound amplification device for his hearing-impaired wife. In 1890, Bell founded the association bearing his name, providing medical and educational information and services for the deaf.

In 1993, the association held its annual conference in Denver; Kenny and Joanna were among the attendants. Lasting three days, it comprised numerous seminars on various subjects. So as to secure the best chance of finding one that might be helpful, Kenny and Joanna split up to try and participate in them all. The hearing-impaired people they met in the process made quite an impression on them - so communicative were these deaf, they could have easily passed as people with normal hearing. Being born with a hearing loss had not consigned them to a life of silence. Kenny and Joanna were very much encouraged.

The AG Bell Association champions an approach to treating deafness known as auditory-verbal therapy, or AVT. This methodology is characteristic for utilizing what little hearing deaf children do have. Most have some. Most, that is, except Alana, who fell into the superlative category of hearing loss. We live, nevertheless, in the age of the bionic ear, or cochlear implant, which can restore hearing even to those disabled as absolutely as Alana can. It was suggested to Kenny and Joanna that she be given one, and thereafter placed into an auditory-verbal program. However, receiving a cochlear implant is not as simple as putting on a hearing aid; as the name implies, it requires invasive, highly technical surgery.

Cochlear implants work their magic by simulating the functions of inner ear cells, reproducing the electrical stimulation those cells would generate in an able-bodied person. The sensory experience that results is not particularly Elysian, having been described as mechanistic, or comparable to hearing underwater. However, to a child born deaf, it is no less a leap forward.

The bionic ear is an Australian invention, and much of the world's expertise on the technology is concentrated in that country. Joanna and Kenny located Doctor Pyman in Melbourne to perform the necessary surgery on Alana. Three-dimensional scanning of Alana's ear revealed she suffered a rare type of inner ear deformity known as a common cavity. Cochlea is the Latin word for 'snail', and it is aptly used to name the key structure of the inner ear, which, absent abnormality, has the appearance of a snail's shell, or a spiral. Alana's cochlea, in contrast, is a simply rounded and hollow cavity. The good doctor had never worked on patients so affected and felt he was not competent to perform the operation. In keeping with the tenacity they had showed up to that point, Joanna and Kenny found and then put Pyman in contact with a German physician who had the requisite experience. Consultation with his colleague reassured Pyman, and, calculating that even should the worst happen it would be no deterioration from the status quo, Pyman decided to push ahead. Because of the difficulties posed by her common cavity malformation, the hardware Alana was implanted with operates at less than ideal capacity. To draw an analogy, a typical consumer stereo system allows for control of the balance of bass, mid range and treble frequencies. At that time, a fully functional cochlear implant has twenty-two such controls, or channels. Alana's has only thirteen. The surgery might nevertheless be labeled, as a relatively miraculous success, given Pyman's initial prognosis.

Alana comes from a bilingual family. Healthy babies have acumen for acquiring any and all of the languages to which they are routinely exposed. However, this is not so for deaf children, as one would expect, even those who, like Alana, benefit from early medical intervention. Now that she had some semblance of hearing, if they wished her to speak with any proficiency, Kenny and Joanna had to settle upon a single language with which to raise Alana. English was chosen: it was the language of her therapist at the time and the one with the widest global currency.

Darkness before the dawn always seems unbearably long. The first ten months after she began her course of auditory-verbal therapy, Alana made no steps towards speech, at least none discernable to either Kenny or Joanna. Then, after the tenth month, she underwent something of a linguistic eruption: words began bursting out from her overnight. Joanna kept detailed notes of Alana's progress. Of that time she wrote, 'it's impossible to shut her up now'.

It was the reward for much dedication. Here are some notable extracts from Joanna's journal that attest to the love and patience that made Alana's progress in the early years of her life possible.

June 6, 1994. (Alana is almost 3 years old)

Just unpacked. Alana has made some progress lately.

1. She can differentiate among car (Bu…), airplane (Ah…), dog (bow-wow), train (Oo-oo-oo-oo), and shoes (walk-walk) by hearing. Those that she is not as certain are cat (meow), cow (moo), and sheep (sh-sh).
2. She will turn her head when we call her name, as if she can hear us and wants to respond.
3. Today, Alana heard the soft ring of telephone. She went over to pick up the phone, and even said something like "hello". This was very surprising since the ring was so soft and she was at the other end of the room.
4. Alana can hear most conversations, except for the sound of "S". Therefore, when talking to her, we have to pronounce "S" louder and longer. We don't have to do so with other phonemes.

Alana looks like a big kid now; she is no longer a little baby. She is very smart. She loves water and games. When she lost interest or her patience, we have to change to some new tricks.

June 7, 1994.

I forgot to mention: a few days ago when I was playing the piano, she didn't want me to keep playing, so she shook her head and said something like "no".

Tonight, she wanted to turn off the TV but did not succeed. I said "uh-oh", and she also said "uh-oh". Obviously, she already started paying attention to our conversation, and likes to repeat what we say.

The journey began with a life-shattering revelation and had taken many frustrating turns on its way. It had led Kenny and Joanna from hope to desperation, and from desperation to hope again. It had been at once filled with the disastrous and the miraculous. It was a tale that, on the scale of familial life, was legendary in its proportions.

And it continues. For Joanna, it took just a single word out of Alana's mouth to give worth to the whole ordeal. Alana's example converted her mother wholeheartedly to the auditory-verbal faith. Joanna had to preach the good news.

Chapter 3

Light in Darkness

Joanna's determination to help her own daughter is worthy of legend. Her willingness to take what she learnt and selflessly share it with the children of Taiwan is worthy of praise.

March 11, 1999 was a day in Joanna's life weighty with excitement. President of Taiwan Deng-Hwei Lee was scheduled to visit the Children's Hearing Foundation on behalf of the 'Organization for the Protection of the Physically and Mentally Handicapped'. Having set out early for the office that morning, Joanna found that hers were not the only nerves on edge. She happened to be the last of the Foundation's staff to arrive. The others were already there, ready and waiting for the VIP.

The announcement of the visit had come to her as something of a surprise. Months prior, Kenny and Joanna had attended a banquet commemorating the political independence of the Central American republics Honduras, Costa Rica, Nicaragua, Guatemala, and El Salvador. The Salvadoran Ambassador to Taiwan, David Ernesto Panama, and his wife happened to be Foundation board members, and at the dinner brought the Foundation and its work up in the conversation with President Lee. The President, his interest piqued, pledged to fund well over 100,000 US dollars to the charity, to be ceremoniously handed over on March 11.

The event preparation had been accompanied by many sleepless nights on Joanna's part. There was so much she wished to squeeze into what was a rather tight window of opportunity. Joanna's charisma and grace served her well on the day. She gave a wonderful presentation, which clearly communicated the mission of the Foundation. Alana was there with her mother as a showcase of the results auditory-verbal therapy could achieve. Of course, Alana did not have sole purchase of the limelight. There were song and dance performances by other Foundation pupils, and visual art shows, from which it was clear that 'disabled' was more than a slight misnomer for the school's children. Joanna's journal entry for the day reads,

"During President Lee's visit, our emphasis was not on the deaf children's outstanding performance in hearing, speaking and academics, but instead, our purpose that day was to show where we need the government's help. Our main focus was two-fold: firstly, the importance of comprehensive hearing tests for infants, and secondly, setting up a support system of touring teachers for the deaf children who went to the normal school system.

When touring the eight counseling and treatment offices at the Foundation, President Lee saw many young children and parents who were in the midst of learning AVT. He was extremely touched by what he saw, and said, early treatment and education is the key task, and the government would start assisting as much as possible right away."

Joanna was hopeful and committed to the work ahead. She knew a presidential endorsement was no panacea. However, it did herald something new. Her sense of mission never left her. Neither too did the pressure that mission entailed.

* * *

Joanna had been convinced that auditory-verbal therapy, in combination with cochlear implantation technology, could compensate for any hearing loss. It was a conviction and the product of personal experience. She envisioned her story being of help for other families with deaf children, a kind of lamp along the road guiding fellow travelers. Her hardship could be considered a blessing for serving as such an example.

Awareness of auditory-verbal therapy in Taiwan was far from widespread. Joanna took her first step towards establishing the Foundation when, referred by a friend, she collaborated with the National Union of Taiwan Woman Association to organize therapy sessions and tour and speak to audiences around the country. When Joanna's circuit reached Kao-Hsung city, second largest in Taiwan, there was one attendee, Grace, who would come to play a particularly important role in the history of the Foundation.

* * *.

Formerly a nurse, Grace was a mother of three; one of whom, her daughter, had lost her hearing. Grace had, up to the point she discovered auditory-verbal therapy, faced great difficulty in finding treatment for her daughter. She would have enrolled her in the Kao-Hsung School for the Hearing-Impaired were it not for her daughter's age, below that of the youngest preschool classes they offered. Grace looked for alternatives in the surrounding area, finding a second school in Tainan (a city in Southern Taiwan), some two hours by car from her home. It too refused admission to her daughter, who was a mere seventeen days younger than their minimum three years admission age.

Grace described herself back then as a headless chicken, running around desperately looking for solutions. Resident professor at Normal University in Kao- Hsiung, Shiao-Chuan Chen, introduced her to auditory-verbal therapy through one of its practitioners. She began taking her daughter to one-hour classes in Taipei. It was some distance from their home: a ten hour round trip by bus. Grace found the commute intolerable, and one can only imagine how much worse it must have been for her daughter. They opted instead for routine air travel, more convenient, but expensive. In order to devote as much time as possible to her daughter, Grace left her profession. As much as it worked in her daughter's favor, the move ignited something of a financial crisis within the family. Grace used to dream that qualified therapists could be stationed in Kao-Hsiung regularly to help the hearing-impaired children of southern Taiwan. She assumed insurmountable costs would keep such a program within the realm of fantasy.

Grace's involvement in auditory-verbal therapy brought her into contact with Joanna. When Grace put the notion to Joanna, she made a sizeable impression. Joanna was distressed that, while here she was promoting auditory-verbal's merits, there were parents motivated and perfectly willing to participate in therapy without the wherewithal to do so. Joanna concluded that some permanent, free service had to be established to cater to these parents. It was to answer that imperative that she and her husband founded the Children's Hearing Foundation. Its Taipei offices opened in October 1996, with a Kao-Hsiung branch following the year after.

At its birth, the greatest challenge the Foundation faced was finding and recruiting the right people to do its work. At the time, professionally accredited auditory-verbal therapists were in woefully short supply in Taiwan. It fell to the Foundation to train its own personnel. The ambit of what the Foundation did was hence broadened beyond Joanna's original vision. It became more than a pre-primary educational institution, but a tertiary one as well. There were fifteen in the first cohort of student teachers. They were put through an intensive six to eight month long, forty hours a week course.

These so-called seed teachers had their share of doubt about the Foundation's prospects. They were taking a great risk by entering such a select field. If the Foundation were to fold, then all their efforts would be for naught. Other avenues through which to pursue a career in therapy in Taiwan were severely restricted. Understandably then, the resolve of many wavered. Joanna had an emotional interest in retaining these staff at the Foundation. She took the departure of even a single one as a personal failure on her part.

Nevertheless, the Foundation made some remarkable achievements in the way it trained its people. One particularly notable example is the way it modified therapeutic techniques developed for use with English to be applicable for Mandarin Chinese. Besides translating teaching material from English, the seed teachers had to concoct completely new routines for those many facets of Mandarin that have no parallel in English. Taiwan, as has been said, suffered a dearth of qualified practitioners. And as such, progress, though tangible, was incremental. There is still work to be done in devising a truly naturalized set of teaching behaviors in Mandarin.

Every aspect of the Foundation, down to the arrangement of its office furniture, has been finely contrived to serve its mission. The tables found in its therapy rooms have been selected because their proportions are perfect for three people: one therapist, one parent and one pupil. And again, every endeavor made by the Foundation chartered unknown territory.

The genesis of the Foundation is found in a primordial power, that of a mother's love for her daughter. That power animated Joanna. It is what motivated her to manage the Foundation without reward or remuneration of any kind. The golden rule, treat others as you would be treated, was to her no abstract maxim but a summation of how she conducted her life. Her empathy for others sprang from her own experiences of suffering, and the acts of kindness, which flowed from that empathy, bore out her tribulations as true blessings.

Chapter 4

Turn Regrets Into Opportunities

Life's most rewarding opportunities are often disguised as crises, a lesson Fiona learned through her own experiences raising two hearing-impaired children.

On January 4, 2002, the Children's Hearing Foundation held a press conference to promote the merits of auditory-verbal therapy to the press and public. For the purpose of the presentation, a few of the Foundation's pupils and their parents were asked to take part in demonstrations on stage, led by a young girl, Chloe, and her mother Fiona. It began with a video showing Chloe during her first day at the Foundation. She had a boyish appearance, with short hair. In the video, if she spoke at all, Chloe made only unintelligible noises. Now on stage at the age of three, Chloe happily played paper-scissor-rock with her mom, oblivious to the many cameras that were focused on her. She was singing and carrying on, and as she played, Fiona shared her story as a mother with deaf children.

Back in 1990, Fiona had a stable 9-to-5 job as an accountant in a trading company, a wonderful marriage, and a healthy and adorable three-year-old son, Henry. Overall, she was content with her life.

Content, that is, with the exception of one missing piece. Henry wasn't talking yet. In the beginning, Fiona and her husband were not concerned; they assumed that Henry would start in due time. At family gatherings, when the other children cried and yelled, the grandparents would comment on how nice and quiet Henry was. It was not until Henry's first birthday that Fiona began to wonder if something was wrong. She and her husband took Henry to see a pediatrician. That first examination resulted in Henry being dismissed as merely a slow learner, but when more time passed and Henry remained mute, a second round of tests at another hospital revealed that he was suffering a medium-level hearing deficit.

Fiona left the hospital that day surprised, shocked, and confused. At the press conference, she recollected to the audience how the road back home had seemed so long. The little boy holding her hand could not have known why his mom looked so sad. What worried Fiona more than anything else was that Henry, according to the hospital physicians, had passed the critical period in child development when newborns acquire speech: from birth to age three. Consequently, even with a hearing aid, Henry would not be able to learn to say "mom" or "dad" as fast as other kids. It would be a long and challenging process. Fiona's circle began to gossip that, because he was both deaf and mute, her son was somehow less of a person. However, always positive and action-oriented, Fiona told herself that she would never allow Henry to become anything but a well-rounded individual, no matter how much effort it required on her part.

Sign languages have traditionally been the means by which the deaf have communicated with each other and their hearing peers. Rich cultures have developed around each of the various sign languages used by deaf people across the globe. Signing is not without its shortcomings, however; the most significant of which is the exclusiveness of its linguistic community. The number of people among the general population who sign is limited. And so long as they are without any other means of communication, deaf signing people must confine their social interaction to that group. Fiona recognized this reality early after learning of her son's deafness. She felt that it would be in Henry's best interests and, if nothing else, in the interest of practicality that she asked him to adapt to society, rather than asked society to adapt to her son. At the school for the deaf that Henry attended, he was taught the traditional combination of lip-reading and sign languages. Fiona nevertheless held hope that Henry's oral communication skills could be improved.

Henry's school required parents to study with their children, but Fiona's job prevented her from doing so. She had to make a decision. Fiona quit her position at the trading company, taking on a role at the insurance firm Aetna. Aetna's more flexible hours allowed Fiona to participate in her son's education. Nevertheless, the time she spent with Henry was still spare, and so Fiona cherished every single opportunity she had to teach him. Even during the drive to school, Fiona would seize the chance to work on Henry's vocabulary.

Fiona had great concern for the maturation of Henry's personality and interpersonal relationships. An introverted, shy, and uncommunicative child, Fiona feared he would grow up to be a recluse. Therefore, she paid particular attention to Henry's emotional well-being. A child's world is naïve and simple, but there are still occasional crises. One day Henry came home looking bothered by something. As it happened, one of his classmates had asked the other kids not to play with him. Fiona, opting against direct involvement, told Henry to confront the troublemaker, ask him why he had acted the way he had, and persuade him that they would be better off friends. It solved that problem, but Henry was soon to transfer to another elementary school, where the number of students in each class was much larger than Henry was accustomed to. Fiona foresaw that the move would exacerbate Henry's social problems. After talking to the teachers, she again decided to attend the classes with Henry. On the first day of school, Fiona explained to his class that Henry wore hearing aids, gently asking the children not to fiddle with them. Fiona would spend what free time she had at Henry's school, helping teachers with administrative tasks and observing how Henry interacted with other children. When Henry did not show initiative in making new friends, Fiona would become his publicist of sorts. Fiona had a natural knack for socializing. Friendship seemed to follow her around. Fiona helped her son to be proactive. Henry's birthday was September 8, which happened to be a few days after school started. Every year, Fiona organized a simple but pleasant birthday party and invited all his classmates. With help from his thoughtful mom, Henry became more outgoing and performed well academically. He graduated with honors from the elementary school.

Now attending Chung Cheng Junior High School and planning to become a comic book artist, Henry has started to show his talent in the arts. Henry is very popular at school and has been elected to positions of student leadership. Fiona remembered when Henry broke her the news of his election with uncontainable excitement. She teased him that he had to have been the teacher's choice. He retorted, 'no, it was my classmates' choice.' Henry was no longer the shy little boy he once had been. When Fiona complemented her son on his tall and handsome looks, he would once respond with sheepish incredulity, 'yeah, right.' Now he cannot help himself; he has to agree.

* * *

Once Henry was well into elementary school, Fiona and her husband decided to have another baby. They had exhausted much effort searching for the causes of Henry's hearing deficit. There was nothing in the family history, so genetic factors were ruled out. They entertained the suspicion that Henry had suffered an infection some time during his gestation or birth, but no doctor could confirm it. Without a definite explanation of her son's disability, Fiona was extremely careful during her second pregnancy. She paid special attention to her diet and exercise, and took no medication. She and her husband had faith that their caution would deliver them a healthy child.

This time they were blessed with a baby girl. Like Henry, there were inauspicious signs in Chloe's infant behavior. She would sleep though all sounds, even the ruckuses friends and family brought with them when they came to visit. Alarmed that she was reliving her experiences with her son, Fiona had Chloe's hearing tested quite soon after her birth. Chloe did indeed have a hearing deficit. What's more, hers was even worse than her brother's. Fiona did not have time for shock or tears. She had to ensure her daughter received treatment before the window of opportunity for teaching her speech shut. Because of her son, Fiona had contact with other parents with deaf children. Learning of the Children's Hearing Foundation, she enrolled Chloe in its auditory-verbal therapy program before she was a year old.

Anyone who sees Chloe for the first time cannot help but remark what a gorgeous child she is. Chloe is three years old; she has a pretty little face with round black eyes that betray her intelligence. The clarity and lucidity of her oral expression belie the gravity of her hearing deficit. She stumbles only in places where fully hearing adults would fall. Furthermore, she is very outgoing, conversing with strangers at ease. Not at all, like what her brother was at that age, Chloe is unbothered by having to wear a hearing aid. She is a very bubbly and caring girl.

When we interviewed Chloe at the Foundation, her teacher Ms. Su asked her whether she wished me to join in her class. Chloe was quite the autocrat. She said yes unhesitatingly, forcefully commanding me to sit down, not just in any old chair, but the one she decreed. Fiona regularly brings Chloe to her office. Her colleagues, seeing how outgoing Chloe is, often comment "like mother, like daughter." Fiona can't be happier or more relieved.

Starting at such a young age has allowed Chloe to make great progress in her auditory-verbal therapy. She began by attending weekly sessions in June 2001, later cutting back to a lesson every other week. She now has therapy once a month. From Ms. Su's experiences, Chloe's performance is excellent. Ms. Su regards Chloe's pronunciation and vocabulary above average for a student with working parents. Needless to say, the more time parents spend with their hearing-impaired children, the better their progress in therapy.

If there was one flaw Ms. Su could identify in Chloe's speech, it was that she was not a flexible communicator. Most children learn how people deal with different social situations by conscious observation and passive reception of information. They absorb then apply this learning in their own lives. For example, when adults chat, children hear and use the discussion as a reference for their own behavior. Children with hearing deficits do not have the benefit of this exposure to social discourse. When others are talking, they close their ears and show no interest in the conversation. With little by way of reference or experience, they find it difficult to match the register or style of their speech with the social context in which they are speaking. To illustrate, most people, if they wish to join a conversation, are able to interpose themselves in a socially appropriate or acceptable manner. Children with hearing deficits, as a rule, are more awkward in this aspect: they will interrupt others no matter what the topic. This social clumsiness poses a significant barrier to successful interpersonal communication.

Therapy acts in part as a substitute for the experiences that deaf children are deprived. Ms. Su teaches Chloe how to communicate and express herself, and how to improve her pronunciation and broaden her vocabulary. Chloe's contribution to these lessons is a regular source of delight for Ms. Su. A memorable instance occurred when Fiona was writing down Chloe's homework for the week. Chloe told Ms. Su, "My mom is doing my homework; let's not bother her." Such percipience and charm from such a young girl warmed Ms. Su's heart.

In one of Chloe's therapy, the classroom was arranged so that Ms. Su was sitting behind a table covered in toys. Because it means she can play with Ms. Su, or more precisely, those toys, Chloe is invariably excited whenever she attends classes at the Foundation. Chloe entered by jumping over to Ms. Su's side of the table. Her jump caused some of the toys to scatter all over the floor. Ms. Su said to Chloe, 'look, they scattered.' Chloe knelt down, picked up one of the toys and, evidently perplexed as to the meaning of the word, repeated, 'scattered'. Fiona jumped in, 'Chloe, what happened to the toys? They "scattered." It was through this so-called 'teaching by scenarios' that Chloe learnt abstract concepts. On another occasion, Ms. Su had a fish tank filled with water. She put a mermaid on a little bed in the tank, and then took from it some small rocks of different colors. Chloe's assignment was to put the rocks 'around' the bed. Chloe looked first at her teacher, and then at her mom. When she looked as if she was ready to throw all the little rocks in the tank, Ms. Sue stopped her. 'Chloe, I mean put the rocks "around" the little bed.' Chloe, puzzled, tried putting the rocks in the tank one by one. Moving on to the next task, Ms. Su took out some light-green models of little fish, shrimps, and crabs. This time, the teacher asked Chloe to 'pass' these little animals 'over' the mermaid's bed. For Chloe, it was a harder concept to grasp than 'around'. She still could not manage it after several attempts. Demonstrating once more, Ms. Su asked Fiona, 'we learnt this in class earlier. Didn't you practice with her at home?' Fiona, embarrassed, answered 'honestly, no'. After a 50-minute session, Fiona recorded a full page of notes, concerning, among other things, vocabulary and phrases, like 'I combed my hair while I made a phone call' (linking two actions together in the one sentence was something Chloe was struggling with), and the meaning of 'generosity'.

Practice, practice, and more practice. The key to improving a deaf child's speech is parental participation. At the Foundation, each child attends a single hour-long class a week. With such limited time spent with teachers, parents must take advantage of the opportunities that day-to-day life has to offer if their children's oral communication skills are to improve. Fiona uses the time she spends preparing dinner to build Chloe's vocabulary and general knowledge. The bathtub too, as much as the kitchen, can be a classroom. On one occasion when she was being bathed, Chloe began an impromptu recital of an ancient Chinese poem she had learnt at school. She missed one of the verses. Her mother seized her chance and explained the poem to Chloe.

People who lack patience with Chloe frustrate Fiona. One incident still bothers her. Fiona was picking Chloe up from her regular school. She found her out the front of the campus crying. Chloe had been riding a tricycle in defiance off a teacher's request that she return to class. The teacher, to make Chloe comply by force, had pulled her off the tricycle. Fiona snapped, scolding the teacher for not bothering to talk to Chloe. After Chloe calmed down, Fiona brought her to the teacher's office and asked her to apologize. Chloe murmured, "I am sorry, teacher." She was met with a ignorant nod. Fiona was dismayed with the way the teacher had handled the situation. The teacher apparently failed to appreciate that patient and respectful communication was a far more effective way of educating children than blunt authoritarianism. However, when she invited the teacher to discuss the matter further, she was rebuffed.

Ms. Su will confess in private that teachers ought to stay emotionally detached from their pupils. Professionalism dictates it be so, but Ms. Su is too much a loving person. Without fail, she finishes all her sessions with Chloe with a big hug. Their rapport is a point of rumination for Fiona. As she sees it, there are perfectly able people who despite their eloquence only cause conflict when they open their mouths. No amount of instruction will make them more agreeable. Fiona has concluded that there is something else more fundamental to interpersonal communication than attuned hearing or clear speech: a heart that is willing to share love and kindness.

Chapter 5

As Long as There is Still Hope

Speech changed Jason, in just five months. Through speech, his personality bloomed and he showed new passion toward this world.

It was ten o'clock on a Tuesday morning. Grandpa Hsing sat in a Foundation classroom, looking lovingly at his grandson Jason. Jason was playing with a toy train, muttering to himself unfathomably. The teacher, Vivian, asked him, 'Jason, what is this? Ch... Choo....' The boy, still concentrating on the toy, apparently did not catch the teacher's question. 'Choo... Choo....' Vivian repeated her question but Jason was unresponsive. 'Grandpa, you need to practice with him at home, OK?' Jason had made little progress after a full year of therapy at the Foundation.

Grandpa Hsing had a question. Why had Vivian not simply taught Jason the word 'train'? She explained patiently that Jason needed to start from basic phonetics, more easily heard and imitated. Proceeding from simple to complex is a key principle of the Foundation's therapeutic methodology. When teaching "train", a Foundation therapist will begin with 'choo... choo', and then 'train... choo, choo....', and finally 'train'. Grandpa Hsing seemed to have understood the explanation, but persisted in repeating "train" to his grandson when the teacher wasn't watching. Then, what one might mistake for a miracle: Jason, impeccably, said 'train'. However, drowned out by the torrent of garbled utterances that followed, it was nothing more than a fluke.

Every Tuesday morning, seventy-five year old grandpa Hsing took two and a half year old Jason to attend classes at the Foundation. The grandpa and grandson live in Hsin-Chu, about a two-hour drive from Taipei city. Their commute to the Foundation was something of a pilgrimage. They had to take the train, the mass-transit system, and then tackle the final stretch on foot. The labor of traveling, plus the fact that they had to wake at dawn, meant that, by the time he arrived at the Foundation, Grandpa Hsing was ready to go back to bed. He would rub his eyes while the teacher and Jason were playing with clay. We watched Jason play a game where he would echo everything his teacher said. Grandpa Hsing completed the job Jason was doing, giving him an almost involuntarily wry wink. Grandpa looked depleted, and Jason, despite himself enjoying the game, was also yawning. Outside the door, Jason's dad, Charles, was sitting on the couch in the lobby. Twenty-six, Charles also suffered a hearing deficit and was completely mute. Both Jason's grandma and uncle were deaf and intellectually handicapped. In total, four members of Jason's family were deaf. Grandpa was their sole caregiver: most plausibly the explanation of the deepened wrinkles on his face.

Kevin Hsing, in his old age, finds himself stuck with the informal moniker, Grandpa. His life has been as a little boat thrust about in the oceanic swell of history. He settled wherever the waves brought him. Born in 1927, he grew up in Her-Fei county in An-Hwei Province, China. He joined the army as a teenager and moved to Taiwan along with the then-ruling nationalist party government. He was once a gunman stationed in Kim-Meng and witnessed one of the historic wars first hand. Time flew faster than usual during that chaotic period, and not because of an excess of fun. The young boy dressed in an uniform had grown into a man approaching fifty by the time it occurred to him that he should start a family. Through a matchmaker, he met and married a Taiwanese girl in her twenties. His story thus far is not atypical among men of his generation.

Hsing knew his bride suffered both hearing and intellectual disabilities. Not particularly bothered, he was an aging, lonely man who needed someone by his side. His first boy was born, like his mother, with a hearing impairment. This was in the seventies, when not much was available regarding medical treatment and special education for deaf children. At that time, Hsing had retired from the army to become a foundry worker. He was the family's only income earner. Indeed, he took sole responsibility for the management of his household, running errands and the like. His wife was dependant upon him, incapable even of going grocery shopping alone. He worked double shifts and had little time left to tend to the education of his son, even though he wanted to.

Two years after the birth of his first son, Hsing's wife gave birth to aonther baby. The second baby was in an even worse condition. He inherited both of his mother's impairments: they were not spared of heredity's potential cruelty. With two sons with special needs, Hsing decided against having any more kids. When asked if he still remembered how he felt back then, Hsing raised his voice, 'back then, I was really sad….' As though it were pointless to go on searching for a description faithful to the reality of his despair, he left it at that.

About seven years ago, grandpa Hsing retired from the foundry. Charles graduated from his high school for deaf children and found a job as a janitor for the city government. Grandpa's retirement was purely nominal. His responsibilities at home continued. It was a hassle to buy groceries when they lived in the countryside. Grandpa Hsing rented an allotment by the beach nearby their home, making a garden out of it. He planted vegetables in the winter and fruits in the summer, all for his family. If you ever happen to find yourself down that way, the old man can still be seen stumbling across the garden, his back hunched, alone with the sea breeze blowing on his weary face. Quite literarily hand to mouth. Such is how he has lived his whole life.

Perhaps thinking more bodies could help lighten his own burden, Grandpa Hsing arranged for Charles to marry when his son turned twenty. His son's disability made him a challenging match to make. Grandpa found a Chinese girl in Indonesia, in person. She lived a life more impoverished than the Hsings. The roves of the houses around where she resided were made out of coconut shells. Grandpa Hsing thought, growing up like in such difficult circumstances, this girl would be hard-working and perseverant when she moved to Taiwan. Advantageously, she could speak fluent Mandarin-Chinese, Taiwanese, and even Hakkanese. Shortly after Charles married, his wife gave birth to a healthy baby girl. Moreover, because grandpa wanted a grandson, she had a boy two years later. The baby boy for whom Grandpa Hsing had waited such a long time was to be the fourth in his family with a hearing deficit. Grandpa was determined nevertheless that Jason would be the first to overcome the handicap.

Jason woke up from a nap, and his five-year sister brought him into the room where we were sitting. His eyes were half-closed; his hands clasped a blue hairy stuffed monster. Grandpa Hsing said to him, 'Come here, Jason.' He simply stood there: he didn't have his implant turned on. Grandpa flicked a switch on the receiver. You might have thought it was the power button for Jason's personality. His countenance lightened and he morphed into the rambunctious little boy he is. Jason has never been afraid of strangers. He will always greet you with a smile on his face. Jason's excitement can be read on his face and heard in his voice. It looked like he had a lot to say. His sister, who was two years older, was just as friendly to strangers. When asked what her name was, she replied cheekily that she had two. 'One is Ann Hsing, and another one is sis.' Grandpa Hsing would be a proud man indeed, if his grandson were to grow up as confident and articulate as his granddaughter.

Vivian, an auditory-verbal therapist was teaching Jason the concept of categories. In three baskets of different colors, there was a variety of toys. One basket contained animals, another food, and the final basket cars. Vivian linked the sound of the names of the categories with the toys they referred to, building the connection between the two in Jason's mind. Doing so developed Jason's ability to discriminate between categories, the object of the exercise. In the next stage of the lesson, Vivian took all the toys out of the baskets and asked Jason to put each one back into the basket it belonged. 'Jason, where should we put this doggie?' The little boy, with a little dog toy in his hand, stared at the teacher. After some hesitation, he put the dog toy in the middle basket, wherein were found food toys like corn and tomato. 'Jason, that is not correct. Where should we put the dog?' Vivian showed grandpa Hsing how to use common household items to make teaching materials like picture cards. Lack of practice was why Jason had made so little improvement. Blame ought not to be leveled on Grandpa: in his elder years, he has become somewhat forgetful, and he found it a challenge to remember to regularly practice with Jason. Furthermore, he had no one to support him. Hiring a tutor was not financially feasible for the Hsing's, or practical, given the remoteness of their location. The other members of the family could not be relied upon. Jason's mother had, frankly, neglected her parental duties. Admittedly, she had been the one who first brought Jason to the Foundation. But Vivian recalls that she was inattentive during therapy, and that the day that she was asked to practice with Jason at home was the last day she ever showed up. Foundation social workers had tried to reach her by phone, but their calls were rejected. It seemed Grandpa Hsing had miscalculated in supposing his daughter-in-law would be an ideal housekeeper. Jason said 'my mom is upstairs sleeping' during the visit.

The total household income of the Hsing family is less than $1,000 US dollars. The medical bills for Jason's implant surgery were paid mostly out of grandpa Hsing's retirement fund, with $6,700 US dollars worth of help from the Hsing-Chu government. The only financial aid the Hsing's receive for Jason's therapy is $100 US dollar subsidy to cover transport expenses to and from the Foundation. It is a struggle to make ends meet; even grandpa Hsing has at times thought about giving up on educating Jason. His determination has survived the doubts, but only just. The responsibility is sometimes more than his singular effort can meet.

The Foundation was always vigilant to ways in which it could assist the Hsings. Foundation social workers considered fostering Jason out to a family with the wherewithal to provide him adequate care. Finding a suitable foster family proved difficult. The Foundation contacted the city government and asked for their assistance in the search for candidates. They asked other Foundation parents whether they could help. After a lengthy search, they found an elementary school teacher, Shelley Ju. Jason would stay at a learning institute in the morning and in the afternoon go to Ju's school. Foster caregivers are able to practice therapeutic exercise with him in a way his grandpa is not.

A foster home is never an easy place to live. It was especially distressing for Jason, for whom grandpa Hsing meant everything. Ms. Ju remembers how tentatively she moved Jason to her house. She took both Jason and his grandpa to a Foundation playroom, and then asked Hsing to leave. This sensitive little boy sensed instantaneously that grandpa was gone; he rushed out of the playroom and started crying. So Ms. Ju took him to a park across the street from the Foundation to let him cry as much as he wanted, and then to her sister's house to let him play with her kids. On the way to Ms. Ju's home, Jason fell asleep in the car. When it came time to wake Jason, he was sleepy but no longer beside himself. He walked the whole way from the car to his new bed without a stir. He neither cried not fussed. Ms. Ju sat with him as he fell asleep, softly explaining that he was to live with her while she taught him. Ms. Ju remembers tears returning to Jason's eyes, and that he listened to her words with fortitude and understanding.

Time quickly bore out how sound the decision to foster Jason had been. Under Ms. Ju's tutelage, Jason's vocabulary expanded dramatically, as did the repertoire of facial expressions and gesticulation that now went with his speech. After he finished classes at his kindergarten, he would hang about a noodle shop Ju's mother owned. He was full of energy, and enjoyed the fondness of all the staff working in the stores nearby. His learning would grow wherever his foster parent took him. Perhaps as a reflection on Ms. Ju, some of the first new words to leave his mouth included 'McDonald's', 'french fries' and hamburgers'. Life with Ju was a world away from the pent-up environment Jason had known since birth. Ju recounted one instance when her mother was taken ill at the noodle shop and had to be sent to the hospital. Ju took Jason along and let him learn about new words related to the hospital. The next day was a Friday and Jason went back to see grandpa Hsing for the weekend. When Ju saw Jason again the following Monday, Jason asked whether 'granny' still had a headache. Ju was so touched that she almost cried. She thought that it had been one thing for Jason to learn to speak well, but quite another for him to use his newfound ability to show love and care to others.

Ju's support for Jason was critical to his breakthrough. She was eventually called back to her home country, Japan, and Jason went through another two foster families. Then in March 2005, Jing took over. By this time, Jason already had no difficulty articulating his own thoughts and emotions. Jing describes Jason as a bit of a westerner. On one hand, he is brash, physically active and even a little domineering. On the other, Jason is very sensitive.

The responsibility of raising his two grandchildren had been a tribulation on Grandpa Hsing's mind, so he was happy to see Jason growing into his foster family so well. However, he feared that, living apart, he would lose his past intimacy with Jason. He need not have. Whenever Jason farewells the old man, he warmly whispers to him, 'Jason is grandpa's boy'. There is an air of tragic beauty about Grandpa Hsing. As long as there is some glimmer of light in the darkness that has surrounded his life, he will pursue it, leading Jason and his family along with him.

When visiting the Foundation in November 2005, Jason played paper, scissors, rock in a Foundation meeting room. He lost the first two times. The third time, there was a glint in his eye as he studied his opponent, looking to outwit her. And he did. He won. Such was Jason's pride in victory that his cheeks swelled to hide his eyes. Ms. Jing Jing Wu, Jason's most recent foster mom, asked him whether he would introduce himself by telling everyone his name. Jason, pretending to be mysterious, fidgeted and finally answered, 'Tom.'

'How could it be Tom? Isn't your name Jason?' Said Wu. Like he had forgotten some important but elusively difficult to recall fact about his life, he exclaimed, 'oh right, it's Jason'. As if remembering his own name was like remembering his mother's birthday.

In one of the classrooms at CHF, Vivian was giving Jason the lesson for the week. They were playing a more sophisticated version of the categories game. Vivian would name category, such as furniture, stationary, dinnerware, and have Jason give specific examples of items that might fall within that category. Four years ago, simple sounds like 'choo choo' had posed a challenge to Jason. Now, he could fluently say words like, 'table', 'closet', 'pencil', and 'eraser'. Next came relations. Jason would be asked, for example, 'what is the sun like?' It required Jason to exercise his imagination and powers of verbal reasoning to arrive at an answer, such as 'the sun is like a fireplace because it is hot.' Jason's face was animated, on cue with oral responses. His body language was dynamic; as if he was some superstar ready should a paparazzo chance to snap him in the middle of therapy. Jason always appeared so confident in himself.

Noticing the attention he was receiving, Jason became busy again, like a little bumblebee touring around flowers. He was quite restless, playing with chairs, and the seeds in a cup of fruit tea he found in the classroom. He was talkative, and in this respect, indistinguishable from any other hearing child his age. He was not even a shade similar to the way he was at our last meeting. Fluid speech had, back then, seemed a long way off. However, it was clear he had the semblance of a very bright child, if only someone would light the fire of his intellect. Now, several years later, the fire had indeed been lit.

During his time at the Foundation, Jason has progressed from having broken pronunciation and a restrictive vocabulary, to comprehension of abstract concepts, and well developed grammar, logic and conversational skill. At the end of August 2006, Jason became a first grader. Because of Grandpa Hsing wishes that Jason's studies continue in Hsing-Chu city, his time in foster care came to a permanent end once he graduated from his course of therapy at the Foundation. There is concern on the part of Jason's therapist that, if he does not continue his training, he may begin to regress and lose some of the benefit of his time at the Foundation. Vivian's observation was that Jason's relationship with the foster family was always reflected in his performance. Jason is exemplary of the wonders auditory-verbal therapy can work and of the power that lies behind that work, undeniably, love.

Chapter 6

"He is not mute; he just can't hear!"

Lamentation could not help them escape their fate, only action and determination. "We brought this child to the world, and we work to see him grow up happy."

On a beach in Ba-Li, a seaside town outside of Taipei, footprints stretched out aimlessly, from near to far-away places. Calvin and his two sons, a two-year-old and a newborn, walked together on the sand. From her car, Linda watched her husband. The sea breeze rushed in the half-opened windows, but Linda missed it underneath the sound of her thoughts. One rang louder than any other: 'your son is deaf'.

Linda and Calvin learned of their eldest son Matt's hearing deficit around the same time their second child, Warren, was born. The story of their discovery is a familiar one. Matt had failed to learn to speak in the time his mother expected he would. Because Matt was found responsive to some low-frequency sounds, such as clapping and pounding on a table, his physicians were initially undecided as to whether his hearing was indeed impaired. His parents were told to wait until his third birthday before submitting him for hospital tests again. His third birthday came, and he had yet to learn words as rudimentary as 'mommy' or 'daddy'. The prescribed visit to the hospital confirmed it. Matt was deaf.

Linda worked full time while her mother and mother-in-law cared for Matt and baby Warren. It was her mother who first alerted to Linda to Warren's abnormality, when he was just ten months old. When, upon examination, doctors told Linda that Warren, as Matt, had a severe hearing deficit, her world seemed to implode beneath her. Linda and Calvin traced back their family history. Calvin's father had been deaf. It appeared highly plausible that the impairment had been inherited from his side of the family. However, Calvin's brothers and sisters also had their own children, and none of them had hearing problems. Linda speculated that medication Matt and Warren had taken in their infancy might account for their deafness, as an unwanted side affect. Experts themselves could not say what the true cause was with any authority.

On their way back from hearing of Warren's news, Calvin drove Linda and the boys to the beach in Ba-Li, northeast coast of Taiwan. Parking the car, he asked Linda to wait inside while he took the two children for a walk on the beach. It unnerved her. She thought him a man upon the precipice. He was, in the most concrete sense. He was filled with self-hatred. Overcome with grief, he cried out to the sea plaintively, picturing himself giving his sons over to the water. He stepped forward in numbness, but his conscience woke him. He had brought these boys into the world, how could he send them out?

Linda, sitting in the car, saw it all in her mind's eye. She did nothing, gambling on husband's strength. Had he truly hardened his heart to it, there would have been no use trying to stop him. Tears stained her face. After an hour, the three returned. No words were spoken between husband and wife.

* * *

Linda had reacted to Matt's deafness with decision, immediately setting about obtaining for him the best treatment she could, and she was resolved to do no less for Warren. After discussing it with her husband, Linda quit her job so that she could stay at home full time with her sons. Calvin took to his newly acquired status as the family's sole income earner with determination, devoting himself to his work so that he could meet Matt and Warren's medical expenses. The implant surgery for the two boys alone cost NT$1,500,000. During the five years that followed, the family was on a war footing, and so hard were Linda and Calvin fighting for their children.

Before six each morning, Linda would take the two to their respective pre-schools in Taipei. Matt and Warren both took entrance exams for the Taipei School for the Hearing-Impaired, but only Matt went on to attend. Warren went instead to special-education classes at the Taiwan Normal University. Both boys would finish at noon, at which time their mother would pick them up, eat lunch with them and then take them home. While the boys napped, Linda would use the time to make vocabulary cards and pictures for practicing their hearing exercises. The remaining demands of the day were met once the boys had gone to bed for the night. It was not uncommon for Linda to put herself to sleep in the early hours of the morning.

Day after day, they commuted back and forth between Chung-Li, a town 1-hour drive away, and Taipei. Linda remembered when Matt started elementary school, once each week she had to take Warren to preschool in Taipei first before picking up Matt in Chung-Li. Then they went back to Taipei together to take Warren to the Foundation. Linda bought a scooter for the commute in Taipei. The never-ending travel time was a real test of the mother's physical and emotional strength. Linda did not give much thought to it at the time, but now, she can hardly believe she persevered.

There were moments of sentiment when the couple felt inclined to have a third child. They were sobered by the prospect of reliving the hardship Matt and Warren had brought them. They recoiled from the fear of what the child would have to suffer, above all else, the carelessness and thoughtlessness of other people. The insensitivity

Matt and Warren faced was reflected in mundane and trivial things, like riding the bus. Proficient in neither hearing nor speech, the boys were nonetheless filled with curiosity, and would be quite chatty with the bus drivers, for which the drivers themselves had little tolerance. Then there were encounters with strangers. Linda recalls a particular incident in a bookstore. A middle-aged woman happened to want a toy Warren had found in the store, and when he would not surrender it to her voluntarily, she attempted to wrestle it from him. Warren would not be moved. On seeing his stubbornness, Linda remembers the woman asking the shopkeeper, 'do you think he's mute?' It broke Linda's heart. 'He's not mute; he just can't hear!'

In those years, there were times when mother and sons cried leaving the house, and times when they cried returning home. Their own relatives had a hard time accepting the boys. Linda's mother made it a condition of her daughter visiting her home that she keeps the boys out of sight from whatever other guests she might be entertaining at the time. She was even in the habit of telling acquaintances that the boys had been 'healed' of their deafness. At some point, it became too much for Linda. She related to how she confronted her mother, 'You are their grandma. If you don't even accept them as they are, how could you expect others to do so? If you aren't happy to see the boys, we won't visit.'

The relationship between mother and daughter broke down for some time. Linda's mother then began to ask about the boys. She requested they visit. It taught Linda the importance of active, open and candid communication. With her hectic schedule, she was hardly home to take care of her sons. Her mother would complain that she could never find Linda at home. Linda told her husband that, if they had guests, he should explain to them why she was not around. Calvin happily obliged her. The relatives were made aware of what the family was going through and were henceforth more caring. There was not a single-family function that took place without the two boys being called on to join in.

* * *

The brothers now attend elementary school: Matt is in the six-grade and Warren is in fourth. Matt is tall and slim, has a fresh face, and gentle manners. He used to dream about being a model when he was little, 'because models can always wear nice clothes'. Currently he wants to be a news reporter. When asked why he changed his career aspirations, he gave away a shy grin and buried his face in a comic book. Warren has an air of naïve innocence about him. He keeps close to his mom. He completed his homework sitting right next to his mother. The boys cannot keep secrets. They are simple, and tell it as it is. Linda never ceases to be amused by their matter-of-fact-ness. For example, Matt has a textbook that on one page reads, 'no plant will grow out of a marble road.' Matt can giving living testimony to the contrary, he has seen weeds grow out of the cracks of such a road. Therefore, he insists that the textbook is wrong. Matt was assigned homework requiring him to answer questions based on his comprehension of that textbook. When it came to the question concerning plants and marble roads, Linda told Matt to repeat merely what he had read. But Matt gave voice to his own views on the subject. He refused to capitulate to the textbook and its false teachings. Warren is an honest, helpful boy. If he sees his classmate drop something on the floor, he will run over, tap on his shoulder and say, 'hey, you dropped something.' He can be quite insistent when it comes to lending his hand.

It is impossible to overstate the importance of the role teachers play in helping deaf children successfully adapt to normal school life. When Matt was about to become a first-grader, Linda had a meeting with the dean at his school, seeking his assurance her son would be assigned to a patient and compassionate teacher. She was told that while 'our teachers might have problems with disobedient students', they never did with deaf children. Fortunately, every teacher Matt has ever had has been wonderful. He especially liked his third and fourth-grade teacher, Pei-Jing Chang. He was forever wandering into Ms. Chang's office during recess to chat or ask her for help with math homework. Linda is so thankful that her two sons have had teachers who truly cared about them, unperturbed by their hearing deficits.

On December 23, 2001, there was a special Christmas party at Calvin's house. Nearly twenty guests from seven different families were there: they were fellow students and their parents from the kindergarten Matt attended. It was one of a pair of reunions that have been held biannually for the cohort over the last ten years. The conveners are bound by the shared experience of raising deaf children. They meet to give an understanding ear, cheer for each other, and exchange parental wisdom. In 2001, they chose Calvin's house for the Christmas party. Much anticipation surrounded the Hakannese food Linda prepared. The guests started to arrive in the afternoon. The dads talked about men's subjects, while the moms chatted about family matters, and helped in the kitchen. The kids were having a ball playing with one another. The next day, Calvin and Linda arranged a trip for the group to visit the town Yi-Gung, famed for its pottery throughout Taiwan. They visited a potters' workshop, and the children were invited to take turns experimenting with their machines. Matt showed his artistic talents, making a splendid plate with butterfly ornaments. Linda, looking back at the pictures they had taken of the party, was amazed by the irony of life. If not for their children's infirmity, these seven families would never have met or become such good friends.

Her two sons have made Linda more conscious than ever of the need to keep their marriage, and their extended family, together. The boys have profoundly affected their dad's character and temper. He was the father who slammed his fist to the wall and injured his hand after their stroll on the beach. Calvin chose to heal his wounds by showing even more love to his boys, much more than what he received from his own dad when he was young. Calvin neigh on spoiled them. No matter his other commitments, he always tries to take them on outings. One of their favorite things to do together is ride their bikes. They often ride all the way to grandma's house and back. Warren has inherited Calvin's interest in fishing; he could spend a whole night and day fishing with his dad. The boys are very close to their Dad. They do what they can to look out for his wellbeing. They have forbidden him from smoking and drinking, and have instituted their own system of penalties for when he transgresses. He must pay them a fine. Calvin teased them, 'what about you two, what should I do if you boys do badly at school'. The brothers answered, 'no TV then'. It was a fair agreement between them.

Raising deaf children has taught Linda so much. Her brother was in a car accident when he was young, leaving him intellectually handicapped. His mother suffered much stress and strain on his account. Linda remembers nights during her childhood when she would wake in the middle of the night to the sound of her mom crying hysterically in the living room. Linda often wondered what could be capable of causing such abject despair. Her own motherhood gave her the answer. But from it, and from her own mother's support, she learnt too the power of maternal determination, and the joy dedicated parenting can bring.

Chapter 7

Grandma's Love

Grandma Hsu took over the motherly responsibilities for her grandsons, and like any other Grandma, she couldn't be more proud of them.

In Taiwan, people are heard to say that a mother's heart is as big as the sky. Then there is Andrew and Raymond's mother. Her heart certainly had something to do with the sky: it was up in clouds instead of down on earth with her children.

Born deaf, she was an intelligent, attractive woman. Her high school principal, being so impressed by her aptitude, tried to recruit her as a teacher. Instead, she had an arranged marriage and, following the wedding, moved with her husband from Hualien, a city on Taiwan's east coast, north to Taipei. Soon after she had their second son, she told her husband she was leaving for Tai-Tung to become a beautician. Her in-laws opposed her decision: they could not conscience a woman who would abandon her family to pursue her individual interests. They tried to talk her into staying several times, but she wasn't convinced. With suitcases in hand, she walked out leaving behind two toddlers with hearing deficits.

Andrew and Raymond are only one year apart. If something happens to one of them, it will happen to the other. The two boys had been less than healthy as babies. When one had a fever, so did the other, and they would both be sick for days, suffering seizures on occasion. For their grandma, Edna Hsu, rushing her grandsons to the hospital emergency room was routine. Back during her own motherhood, her eldest son had too been born struck by a high fever and seizures. For the first seven years of his life, hospital was like a second home for him and his mother. He recovered from the fever, but the ordeal left him hearing impaired. He went on to graduate from junior high school and become a qualified mechanic. But he still lives in silence, having never learnt to speak. Edna has only the most rudimentary means of communicating with her son. They have enough of a mutual understanding that she can tell him when it is time to eat and when it is time to shower, but nothing further. Her son's mind is veiled to Edna, the most she can surmise is that he is simple and self contained.

Edna was born in a rural town in Tai-Chung in Central Taiwan, to a family of eight children. Economic expedience forced her to drop out of school after sixth grade. Even during those six years at school, she had spent little time studying, needing instead to work part time at a food factory to help support her family. Consequently, as an adult she was close to illiterate. Marriage and motherhood came to Hsu when she was only twenty. When, at forty-five, the grandchildren began arriving, her four sons still lived with her, along with her ninety-year-old mother-in-law. When the matchmaker arranged a marriage with a girl from Hualien, Edna and her husband were very happy that someone else would take over the responsibility of caring for their son. They took in their daughter in law as if she were their own. But even so, she could not fulfill the modest hopes they held for her. They have been out of contact with her for over six years. Her own family is unaware of her whereabouts. Edna was left to care for a household of dependents.

Both Andrew and Raymond were diagnosed with severe hearing deficits. Pre-school is the most critical period for every family with deaf children. The stronger the learning foundation built then, the less difficult will be the deaf child's transition into the mainstream education system and integration into the broader hearing world.

Hsu spent her entire savings on hearing aids for the boys. The government covered other expenses related to their treatment. Were it not for which, Edna's family could not have born the full financial burden. Edna sent her grandchildren to two preschools, one mainstream, the other especially for the hearing impaired. Every day, Edna got up at five, did laundry, prepared breakfast, took the boys to the special school in the morning, attended the classes with them, and then couriered them to the mainstream pre-school in the afternoon.

Enda's first contact with the Foundation was an unexpected blessing. It came about when Joanna visited the boy's school to give a talk on auditory-verbal therapy. Convinced by Joanna's zeal, Edna began taking Andrew and Raymond to the Foundation for therapy once a week.

The Foundation's methodology requires parents apply its principles in every day life. However, the demands placed upon Edna by her family, both physically and emotionally, meant she had little if any time or energy to do so. Moreover, her illiteracy stood in the way of performing many of the boy's exercises with them. Notwithstanding, the two preformed remarkably well during the time they were enrolled at the Foundation; so well, in fact, that they aroused the attention of the local media. Interviewed by a newspaper reporter on her success with auditory-verbal therapy, the old woman had bashed when asked how she taught her grand children, explaining that it had been not her but the Foundation that had taken the lead. Ms. Wei, the boy's former teacher, points out that Edna still played a very important role in facilitating Andrew and Raymond's learning via the family ethic she instilled in her household. Faithful to that ethic, the boys were excellent listeners and willing students. Their good character shone through in their performance. Although the brothers still baulk at questions related to their mother, her leaving them has not come to dominate their lives. They have found love in their grandma's arms.

The cooperation between the Foundation and the teachers at the schools where Andrew and Raymond attended has been a key factor behind the progress the two brothers have made. Home and school visits are strongly emphasized at the Foundation so that its students can be exposed to a singularly integrated, consistent and ubiquitous educational environment. Foundation teachers instruct parents and schoolteachers on how they can best assist the Foundation's work. Ms. Wei will write down a few pointers after class such as that schoolteachers should orally communicate with children of hearing deficit as much as possible, and that they should closely observe the interaction between these children and their peers. It is easy for deaf children, because of their difficulties with communication, to become isolated from others and discouraged from learning. Ms. Wei will, moreover, share her insights with her counterparts at her pupils' mainstream schools. Thereby, all those who play a part in the deaf child's upbringing work in unison. It takes preparation and adjustment. Most schoolteachers are not experienced in teaching deaf children, so the Foundation provides support and advice whenever needed. Fortunately, more and more schools in Taiwan have begun dedicating resources to attend to the needs of students with disabilities. Once Taiwanese society starts recognizing the special needs of deaf children, one can expect the help presented to them will be even greater. With all that support, deaf children will be able to grow up to repay the favor, as full contributors to community life.

May is the season of carnations. The smell of the flowers seems to reflect the sweetness of motherly love. To celebrate Mother's Day, Edna and her grandsons were asked to be photographed together. Edna had rarely had her picture taken. She sat in the corner of the classroom, looking rather nervous. The two boys next to her had big smiles on their faces. When Edna pointed out that picture at the Foundation, she observed 'Andrew is very outgoing and energetic. Raymond looks more like his mother but has his dad's personality.' Edna's pride in her grandsons is nothing out of the ordinary. She is devoted to them.

Chapter 8

An Endless Marathon

'Thinking about what kind of future he will have makes me so scared and worried'. To raise a child like this is to run a marathon with no end.

The first time she saw Harry, 'granny' felt a special bond with him. They were not related. Granny was a mid-wife when she was young, and now provides traditional Chinese medical treatment and therapy. The invalidity of her own children inspired her to become a student of Chinese medicine. She learned massage and acupuncture with a view to treating her children, but, incidentally and not in accordance with any design on her part, she developed a wide reputation as a healer. Harry's parents heard about her in the midst of despair. Their son had turned two and was yet unable to stand up, let alone walk. They had been taking him to physical therapy, but Harry was an unwilling recipient, hysterical whenever he visited the clinics. Disillusioned by his lack of progress, when Harry's parents Sean and Sharon Ling heard of 'granny', they decided they could do no wrong giving her a call.

Granny offered to treat Harry for free every evening. She would in essence be massaging Harry's back to stimulate the nerves along his spine, a procedure that would be over in around thirty seconds. Therefore, at the end of every working day the Ling family trekked back and forth from granny's house for the thirty-seconds of treatment. Many of granny's patients abandon the course of therapy half way to completion. However, the Ling's persevered. Brevity aside, the massage appeared to be invigorating Harry's weak body, energizing it. Within three months of seeing Granny, Harry could sit up. And two more years he was walking. Those steps, small as they were, had all the force of his parent's determination behind them. Even Sean got teary-eyed. However, walking was just the start of Harry's problems.

Harry was born into a family of four living generations. His great grandmother celebrated his birth alongside his mother. In spite of the goodwill that surrounding him from the off, his life began inauspiciously. He was diagnosed with a hereditary, potentially terminal heart disease. Moreover, he was blind in his left eye. Harry has spent most of his life in a pediatric ward, a residency broken up by stays in intensive care stays, which have at times lasted up to three weeks. At two weeks old, he underwent a triple by-pass. There was a complication in surgery and his vocal chords were damaged. Harry's voice remains scratchy today as a consequence. Of more immediate concern then was that the injury prevented Harry from swallowing. After being discharged following the heart surgery, he was kept on fluids, injected into his stomach through a tube inserted in his nostrils. Needless to say, feeding him that way was far from easy. The hospital staff trained Sharon and her mother-in-law to operate the cumbersome equipment, but even so, their competence left something to be desired. A mistake could have led to Harry being chocked to death. Sharon resorted to feeding Henry milk with a spoon. It meant trading off efficiency for safety: there was unlikely a slower way to do it. The endeavor would occupy Sharon and Sean for whole nights.

The Ling family received confirmation Harry had some degree of hearing impairment soon after he was born. Harry's multiple physical disabilities meant that performing a subjective hearing test on him was neigh on impossible, since it could not be determined which specifically among his myriad of handicaps would account for the results of such tests. Hence, even now, the severity of Harry's hearing deficit is unknown.

The Lings were advised not to have Harry fitted with hearing aids until he was able to sit up. With doubt lingering over the gravity of his impairment, Harry's surgeon withheld approval for a cochlear implant.

Harry, as can happen to children with multiple disabilities, was left without specialized care because institutions treating intellectual disability would claim that, as a hearing impaired child, he was outside the ambit of their expertise, and vice versa. Sean never anticipated that difficulty, and much time was wasted negotiating, sometimes pleading, with special schools to obtain admission for Harry.

Their arguments make sense from the schools' perspectives. Children with multiple disabilities are best educated by composite targeting of their impairments, that is, by integrating treatment rather than partitioning it. Such is currently unavailable among the special schools in Taiwan, certainly not encompassing the range of handicaps Harry suffers from. It is not unheard of elsewhere in the world. The University of North Carolina has established what they have deemed 'Division TEACCH', standing for the 'Treatment and Education of Autistic and related Communication-handicapped Children'.

Sharon learnt of the Foundation through a co-worker. Burnt by their experiences at other intuitions, she and her husband were pessimistic about Harry's chances of admission. The Foundation is flexible in whom it chooses to provide its services to; so long as there is some prospect its therapy will be to a child's benefit, that child is welcome at the Foundation. On evaluation, Foundation therapist found Harry a suitable candidate for intervention. Sean took responsibility for taking Harry to his Foundation classes, since he worked in the family business and had a more flexible schedule. Harry's improvement was undeniable, if gradual. One day when attending a class, he confirmed that he could hear. Harry passed a milestone in his life and the life of his parents, a milestone late in coming to be sure, but joyous nonetheless.

Now in his pre-teens, Harry's outlook is promising. Admittedly, he is smaller than most boys his age, and walks with an unsteady gait. However, his heart has grown stronger as he has grown older, and there are plans to repair surgically his damaged vocal chords.

When observing Harry in a class at the Foundation, it is easy to be impressed by the patience Sean showed toward him. The two were playing a card game. On the cards, there were characters dressed in different uniforms according to their professions. The therapist would ask Sean to say words related to the professions, and ask Harry to find the cards that matched that description. The game worked on both Harry's listening abilities and the way he processed the information he heard. Harry made mistakes, in one case when Sean repeated: 'fire trucks', 'fire'. 'Must be that he rarely sees fire trucks'.

Sean was tolerant, but not to the point of permissiveness. During the same therapy session, Harry accidentally collided his hand with his therapist's head. Sean asked his son, firmly but with a smile, to apologies. Harry would not, and instead shook his head. 'Say "I am sorry" to the teacher,' his dad repeated. To Sean's mind, his son's handicaps are not a license to escape discipline. He explained afterward that he and his wife were taking particular care to inculcate polite manners in their son, so that he will be able to defuse any offence he may inadvertently cause by his hearing or speech.

You would never know from speaking with Sean and Sharon how truly tumultuous life with Harry has been. Their turmoil has exceeded what families with deaf children can expect to face. The placidity throughout has come as result of the support of their whole family, tangible and intangible. Like Harry's great grandmother. That she never stopped loving him because of his physical limitations has been a source of immeasurable worth to his parents. The power of love in the family may seem ordinary, but it is strong enough to overcome any obstacles in the world. The Ling family serves as a living proof.

At one point, Sean and Sharon were planning the summer for their son. They wanted to take him on a trip to Japan. Harry was very excited about going to the birthplace of his favorite cartoon characters. He is becoming quite an opinionated person, he makes sure his views are understood. When speech fails him, he turns to the written word. At home, there is always a white board ready for him.

Adolescence lies around the corner. Sean and Sharon's fretfulness towards Harry has not mellowed with age. Sharon jokes that she dare not even think about what she will do when it comes time for Harry to strike it out on his own, find a job and start a family. The journey of his life has been like an endless marathon. There is no doubt she and Sean will give all they have to keep running alongside their son.

Chapter 9

Where There is love, There are miracles

On his childish face was a pair of silver-framed glasses, which made him look like a little professor. Books and magazines on history and geography were all over the shelf in his study: they all belong to Dylan. He was six years old and about to become a first grader.

Silver-rimmed glasses hung precariously off the tip of his nose. Dylan looked the very image of a boy professor. He was not so much playing with his blocks as undertaking some scientific investigation of them, muttering his findings to himself. His analysis finished, he took a tome on dinosaurs from his shelf and began an earnest study of it. This particular shelf was filled with books and magazines on a variety of subjects, from history and geography to astronomy. Dylan's Mum, Shelley, commented on how Dylan clung to every single word he saw, like a true bookworm. Shelly had a newspaper on her lap. When Dylan raised his head and saw it, he came over and began to read it aloud with her. Each word sounded from his mouth clearly and accurately. At the time six years old and ready to start first grade, Dylan was, as now, severely hearing impaired.

Shelley is a schoolteacher. Hers is one of the few but fortunate careers to be motivated by passion. Shelley holds a longstanding desire to help children find, cultivate and use their talents. She was a woman with ever-higher expectations, which were therefore a cause of great frustration as well as joy. Few students or their parents could match what Shelley would have described as her own enthusiasm for learning. However, after having a son, she came to view her work in a new light.

The delight Shelley felt at Dylan's birth was not long in lasting. The news that he suffered a severe hearing deficit was too much for her to bear. Her tears kept her awake for many nights during his infancy. Like so many of the parents no one could tell Shelley or her husband the cause of Dylan's impairment. One doctor suspected that Dylan was born with an inner ear deformity. Hypothesized to be an externally inflicted injury to the head, brought about by a fall or some other collision after birth, was to blame. Inexplicability makes accepting deafness that much harder.

The birth of any child is life changing, but no life arrives with more earth shattering force than a disabled one. For many parents, as we have seen thus far, thoughts of the future, and the gravity of the task of raising their child, can be torturing. For parents with deaf children, their initial shock is followed by a series of questions. What is the true severity of the child's impairment? Will hearing aids be needed? Which supplier is the best choice? Is a cochlear implant necessary? Which hospitals have the facilities and staff to perform the required surgery? How much will it cost? What kind of education is needed and which institutions will provide it? How much improvement can we expect to see in the child's speech and hearing?

Shelley was no exception; she felt confused and overwhelmed. However, through her maternity ward, she was exposed to a support group of mother's in positions similar to her own. They were of immense help to her. Sharing their experiences of child rearing not only provided these women with answers. It relieved the stress and pain they had felt, lifting their spirits to restore the joy that ought to rightly accompany parenthood.

Certitude was far from forthcoming as to what could be done for Dylan. Physicians at the Taiwan University Hospital advised Shelley that it would be best if medical intervention were forgone entirely. Doctors at Taipei's Veteran's Hospital came to a starkly different conclusion, prescribing steroid treatment to stimulate the growth of Dylan's hearing nerve. The injections Dylan received swelled up his face, but not much else.

For Shelley's husband, Jake, patience was becoming something of a scarce commodity. Jake was an engineer; he had an analytical, problem-solving mind. He believed not in lamentation but action and solution. A cochlear implant was the next alternative and was suggested he and his wife consider. They consulted Joanna at the Foundation. Her advice was, of course, that such an implant was essential if Dylan's deafness was to be remedied. Jake was in favor of it from the start. Shelley was hesitant, thinking about how young her son was. The couple researched the procedure extensively, and found that it had, at that time, been successfully performed on babies as young as a year old. Dylan's age ought not to have concerned them. They asked Joanna a final question, if Dylan was her son, would she have agreed to surgery? The reply: without hesitation was, "yes". They resolved to go ahead. It was the right decision. Recall that timing is critical to successful implantation, and the timing of Dylan's surgery was optimal.

What visually differentiates a deaf child from other able-bodied children is the hearing aid worn in his or her ear. If the child has a cochlear implant, he must carry a small microphone and a palm-sized device called a speech processor. Dylan is always happy to demonstrate his kit. His mother is thinking of replacing his microphone with another more vibrantly colored one. He is unique in that respect. Shelley knows of parents who try to find black hearing aids for their children, so that they will be hidden beneath their children's hair. In addition, some ask their children to remove their hearing aids when they have visitors. Children themselves are accustomed to leaving their hearing aids at home when they go out, to evade curious looks from strangers on the street. Without hearing aids, they can hear nothing, and if they are not hearing, they are not learning to speak.

It perplexes Shelley. These children are in fact different. Why bother trying to hide it? How can they learn to value themselves and stand on their own feet in the face of that kind of antipathy? She always reminds her son of his importance to her. When in public, if other children are quizzical about Dylan's hearing aid, she asks him to explain to them what it is, to a typically warm and interested reception. She has also bought a bunch of colorful bags for Dylan's language processor. Any kid who sees it wants to touch it.

Shelley's opinion is that parents must recognize the strength and weakness of their children. They need to accept the latter while embracing the former. She takes instruction from the life of a young deaf man she is acquainted with. Self-acceptance eluded him as a child, driving him to the point of attempting suicide. At nineteen, he finally resolved himself to his disability, had cochlear implant surgery and learnt to speak. Though perfect speech is something he is unlikely ever to attain, nevertheless what he has achieved has made his life infinitely more abundant.

Shelley keeps a notebook to record Dylan's progress: new words added to his vocabulary, phrases and pronunciation needed to be practiced, and so forth. Shelley has recorded every detail every day. Like all the Foundation's successful cases, Dylan's performance is the result not merely of direct tuition, but of living in an environment amenable to successful learning. The Foundation focuses on practical listening techniques. An example would be hand cueing, which is, covering one's mouth while speaking to a deaf child, to force him or her to listen and not lip-read in conversation. Therefore, the theory runs, reliance on lip-reading stymies progress in learning to listen. Hence, Shelley makes an effort to be consistent in hand cuing whenever she speaks to Dylan.

Shelley applied for a leave of absence so she could take care of her son. She was convinced that Dylan needed to learn as many new words as possible; rich speech and rich thought flow from having a rich vocabulary. She used index cards with picture on one side and the vocabulary on the other. Dylan first familiarized himself with the pictures, absorbing the meaning of the word before committing its sound to memory. He would then move on to constructing sentences with the new word. Some words serve as germs for the growth of a child's vocabulary, words like 'why'. By asking 'why', Dylan could invite conversation and thus opportunities to practice speaking. Shelley also asks Dylan 'why' often, to train him to explain things. If Dylan says: 'I'm hungry', Shelley will ask him 'why are you hungry?' Such confrontation can be, at first, not a little bemusing, so hints were initially in order. 'Because you didn't eat much at lunch.' Shelley would follow with another question: 'why didn't you eat more at lunch?' These exercises cultivated Dylan's communicative skill and confidence, to the point where he would volunteer his opinions, insights and queries unprompted. His readiness to speak up has at times been a source of amusement for his mother. As on one occasion, when, driving in the countryside, Dylan asked, 'did congee grow out of a rice patty?' Shelley couldn't help but burst out laughing.

As Dylan became more and more proficient with language, he fell in love with reading. Shelley bought all kinds of books to satisfy his newfound interest. She prioritized books on language, and then natural science. She also bought picture books, to engage Dylan's creativity and imagination. Dylan began keeping a daily journal. In the beginning, each entry was only ever a single sentence long, but gradually, they became more and more extensive. Shelley would write with him, treating the diary as an exercise in correct expression. It improved Dylan's grammar tremendously. Dylan's grasp of verbal style is more sound even than his hearing peers. He is a successful example of the Foundation's auditory-verbal methodology. By integrating formal training with day-to-day life, the Foundation has helped hearing impaired children reach the limit of their potential by immersing them in a constant and consistent learning environment.

Being witness to her son's development gave Shelley a new view on education. She now sees learning from the perspective of the pupil. She is no longer as demanding as she was before motherhood. She now considers it far more important that children be taught to value and respect themselves and others, as they are. Such, and not squeezing high marks out of students, ought to be the first priority of educators.

Dylan is now a local celebrity. He has been invited by newspapers, magazine, and radio stations to share his story. The little seed of hope Joanna put in Shelley's heart years ago has bloomed. What Dylan has achieved is not a miracle; it was a reward of his family's love and affection.

Chapter 10

Marching Forward: A Mother's Tender Heart

To be a divorcé mother is to be in an unenviable position. Nevertheless, Silvia takes endless delight in her son. His happiness is her happiness. Nothing else matters.

Another day, another session. Ms. Hong, punctual as ever, found her classroom empty. It was one of numerous late showings in which Silvia had forgotten to take her son Aaron to therapy at the Foundation. Something was not right. Ms. Hong had been Aaron's dedicated tutor since his first day of therapy. She had built a trusting relationship with the mother-and-son pair. She was soon to learn from Silvia the explanation of her absent-mindedness. 'Aaron's dad and I got divorced.'

* * *

The streets of Taipei in the winter are always filled with cold and moist air. Aaron's home is an aged apartment. The entry way was dark and decorated with scrapped advertising fliers. A young woman answered the door. With a delicate face and a white sweater, she introduced herself as Silvia.

The intimacy between mother and son in that household was undeniable. Aaron was brimming with childish energy, excitedly, rather incorrigibly, running about Silvia's feet. Giddy and wishing for attention, he would bark or make noise with the family television in order to attract our focus. He would interrupt discussion with his mother by requests, motivated as much by restlessness as anything else, for cookies or smething else. However, from the way she handled his disruptive excitement, there could be no doubt how much she loved and cherished him.

* * *

Silvia is a hairdresser by trade. It was through her resident hair salon that she met her now former husband. He was an auto mechanic and 10 years her senior. She married at just 21. Taiwanese say much older husbands are apt to take better care of their wives. Folk wisdom did not hold true for Silvia. She describes her ex-husband as extremely generous to friends, but not family.

It is said, the root of all evil, and Shelley's marital strife, began with money. Silvia left the workforce to become a fulltime mother once Aaron was born. Her new husband was not much of a breadwinner. He never could hold down stable employment. If he had money in his pocket, he spent it either on entertaining his friends, or lending it to one of them. Silvia found herself unable to afford life's essentials, while her husband only ever complained that she was always nagging him for money. It was a domestic arrangement in terminal decline. Silvia had to find ways to make ends meet. Doing odd jobs from home, the most she could manage was a meager 15 to 30 US dollars a night. Her ex typically slept while she worked through to the morning, and offered little to no help besides.

* * *

From his birth, all was, in everyone's estimation, well with Aaron; nothing signaled other than that Aaron was in normal health. It was at eight months of age, during Chinese New Year festivities, that Silvia first became aware something was awry. The holiday is marked by fireworks, but whereas the noise kept Silvia awake at night, Aaron slept soundly through it.

Recalling that Aaron was born with lower-than-average weight, plus spasms in his feet, Silvia's first suspicion was that Aaron was epileptic. But a visit to a specialist disconfirmed that theory. On the suggestion that she do so, Silvia had Aaron's hearing test, resulting in a diagnosis of severe hearing impairment. However expectable the news was, Silvia met it with incredulity. Even talking about it now, she has disbelief in her voice. She sought several other opinions on the matter, but there was no dissension. She was instructed that Aaron required a cochlear implant. However, the cost of almost $22,000 US dollars was more than what she and her husband could afford. Their immediate family, at first vocal in their support for Aaron, became quiet as soon as they heard the expenses.

Silvia could have been forgiven for despairing. Fortuitously, around that time, she saw a news report that a hospital, Chang-Gung, was offering financial aid to families having cochlear implant surgery. They would partially reimburse the medical fees, and provide the implant, the device it self, for free, meaning the total cost would be 15 percent of what it otherwise would have been. Within a month of his first consultation at Chang-Gung, Aaron's surgery was complete.

Alongside his hearing impairment, Aaron was born with inner-ear imbalance and delayed physical development. He was incapable of running because of poor hand-and-foot coordination. When he was a toddler, Silvia had Aaron attend physical therapy, scooting him back and forth from the hospital in all seasons. Aaron did eventually learn how to walk, but not without emotional travail, felt by his mother more than anyone else.

* * *

Silvia first heard about the Foundation from her sister, who, in turn, became aware of it through the radio. She enrolled Aaron, and he became a Foundation regular. Ms. Hong, his therapist, has, more or less, seen the boy grow from infanthood before her eyes. The Foundation opened Silvia's mind to how pervasive hearing impairment was in Taiwan.

Silvia was eagerly looking forward to her son's first word. When finally came, it was, 'Daddy!' She refused to believe it. The irony seemed to be lost on her, she found it anything but humorous. After all, it had been she, not daddy, who had been the one walking alongside Aaron every step of the way.

Her husband was hardly there. When Silvia finally left, she did so without asking a penny of him. With no money, she had no choice but pawn off all of her belongings, wedding gifts included, but the proceeds from the fire sale amounted to less than $1000 US dollars. She and Aaron moved to a studio apartment, and then to their current residence. Now as before, she relies upon contract work to sustain herself and her son. She has little access to government support. Under Taiwan law, single women have their parents' income pooled with their own for the purposes of calculating welfare benefits. Consequently, Silvia has been disqualified from receiving any. Silvia is carrying herself and her son alone.

* * *

Good things come to those who wait, and there is no denying that it takes time for children receiving therapy at the Foundation to learn to talk. Silvia paid full attention to Ms. Hong's instructions. Silvia and Aaron made best use of the limited space and resources available to them in their home. Raising and teaching Aaron, alongside her work, came to consume Silvia's life. In her experience, one of the advantages of the auditory-verbal approach is that it can be personalized, tailored to the details of a specific child's life. Ms. Hong told me she was very impressed with Silvia's persistence. Aaron would stumble. However, Silvia never stopped.

The process was long, but gradually, Aaron learned to talk and converse. Gradual indeed, Silvia was driven with anxiety whenever Aaron's rate of improvement slowed. Her latest concern was that Aaron had yet to move beyond short sentences, such as, 'Mom, I want this.'

When the time came for Aaron to begin attending preschool, Silvia was reluctant. She feared, not without cause, that he would face harassment because of his disability. He would be an easy mark, because the same disability that stood him out for abuse also made it hard for him to fend for himself. Silvia was therefore, and understandably, quite particular in her choice of school. It had to have compassionate staff, and a small student cohort. She found one that fit the criteria, and, moreover, one whose principal was also generous enough to offer her a payment plan within her means. As it turned out, Silvia's fretting over Aaron's vulnerability had been for naught. If there was one student at his preschool who could afford to dampen his aggression, it was Aaron. The preschool was good to him. Hanging around other kids his age 'expanded', shall we say, Aaron's vocabulary, to his mother's amusement.

* * *

As Aaron grows, so the people around him change. To further aid his grasp of language, and maybe to offset the influence of his peers, the Foundation secured a grant from the Rotary Club to hire a speech tutor. This tutoring went on for more than a year with three different tutors. Valuable as it was, the tutoring ended when Aaron entered first grade. More significantly still, after many years of working with Aaron, Ms. Hong left the Foundation. With her departure, Silvia has decided that Aaron was ready to 'graduate', and he no longer attends the Foundation.

That year, 2005, Aaron became a first-grader. It was a milestone passed with nervousness on Silvia's part. The number of students per class at his elementary school is at least double what it was at the preschool. The possibility that, lost in the mire of other children, Aaron would fail to receive the attention his needs demanded was a real one. A few days before school started, Aaron's teacher to be rang Silvia to arrange a meeting. At their encounter, she informed Silvia that she had experience teaching the hearing impaired, easing Silvia's mind somewhat, but not to such as to stop her lying awake all night before Aaron's first day. The chaos school life could bring was unrelenting.

Silvia obtained permission to stay in the classroom with Aaron that first day of school, though only for that one day. Separation from parents, as with textbooks and tests, is part and parcel of the move to elementary school. She had to learn to let go. He, too, has to learn to look after himself without mother's intervention.

Because of the solid foundation laid in pre-school, Silvia is confident about Aaron's academic prospects. On the social side of things, Aaron gives no appearance of timidity. Rather, he is a bit of a mover and shaker, as far as elementary school students go, something of a boss. His classmates might even be described as his underlings. Silvia laughed nervously when she describes her shock at how macho her son is, being so young.

Given that Aaron has adapted so well to his new school, Silvia has begun to entertain thoughts of returning to her profession. With caution, it must be added. Even though Aaron spends lots of time at school now, she still feels she must be at home at the ready, incase. Shortly after school started, Aaron received a knock to the head. Silvia rushed to school with her heart pounding fast, concerned his implant might have been damaged, though she need not have been.

* * *

Silvia commented, 'I would talk of suicide when I was 17, 18 years old. But now, I do everything to keep myself strong. Otherwise, what would happen to my boy? I believe all single parents share my feelings.'

Chapter 11

Feeling Sounds in Silence

To communicate with her dad, Ann learned sign language. Their discussions are invariably accompanied by outlandish gestures, back and forth, non-stop. Even Ann's sister complains, 'They are so "noisy"!'

November 2005, the "99 Degrees Celsius" art center in Taipei city: on display in the enormous space were sculptures made of steel and copper. Taking as their subject human facial features and body parts, the pieces included a waving hand and a portion of a female figure. The sensation elicited by the lines and curves was simultaneously one of strength and delicacy, as if warm blood flowed beneath the cold metal surfaces. Critics labeled it 'refined steel turned silky smooth'.

One piece was half of a face. A huge hole gaped from under the nose, and from this orifice came tremendous bursts of air. Titled 'shouting', the experience of appreciating the work was very unique: one could not hear the sound, only felt it, and the desperate desire to communicate with the world outside.

* * *

In drizzling rain, the community shuttle bus meandered through the mountainous countryside. It was on the winding, convulsive road to Ann's house. Ann's father was Mr. Liang-Tsai Lin, an artist.

A few paintings of striking colors adorned the walls of his house. Most of these recent works of his have been inspired by the Taiwanese aboriginal culture. Because of his hearing impairment, he could not hear or talk. He explained the paintings by writing on a tablet.

From his signing, handwriting, animated facial expressions and bodily gestures, Lin had a lot to say. Living in a silent world, he was far from a quiet person.

* * *

Born in 1947, Lin grew up on a farm in Zang-Hwa county in Southern Taiwan. He was born deaf. He was oblivious to his playmates teasing or gossiping behind his back. However, his childhood was trying, and less than colorful, Lin learned to entertain himself. He would go fishing in the river, or watch geese and ducks swimming in the pond. Exposure to nature cultivated his talents in the arts, and his brushstrokes came to express what speech could not.

Lin's father was a government employee and worked hard to sustain his family. He always encouraged Lin to paint. Lin attended the National Art School on the recommendation of his school for the deaf. After graduation, he and his fellow alumni formed a business partnership of painting reproductions for export. It was monotonous work, first compelled by financial necessity and then by irresistible success. It was as the enterprise began to flourish that Lin was struck by a personal tragedy. He was burgled, and his life-long collection of paintings stolen.

Having lost it all, Lin had no choice but to begin again. To start afresh, he left Taiwan, learnt French and traveled to Belgium to study at the Royal Academy of Fine Arts in Antwerp. He planned to major in oil painting. One year into the study, he made a daring move: with no previous experience in the form, he enrolled in the Academy's sculpture department. With steel and copper as his medium, he looked to the human body as his subject. He banged, cut, and broiled to show muscle strength with simple, abstract lines. He put his feelings into his work. Sculpting, he explained, requires good ideas and diligent hard work. It entails 'a lot of work with the hands and very little with the mouth'. It's perfect for 'what I am trying to say is already in the work itself'. He graduated at top of the class in 1989, not without grey hairs to attest to the stress.

In one of the short trips back home during his study abroad, Lin met Miss Jang Jeh, then a boutique shop owner. Jeh later became his wife.

Lin always thought his deafness was non-hereditary, the result of a fever he had as a young child. Following the birth of his first daughter Ann, neither he nor his wife paid particular attention to her hearing. Many a time, as we have seen, fireworks are to thank for first illuminating a child's deafness, and so it was in Ann's case. When she was four months old, she slept through a round of them. Alarmed, Jeh began to tap hard on the crib, wall, closet, and everything else in sight that made sounds. Ann lay undisturbed, in tranquil oblivion.

On confirming Ann's deafness, Lin was given a choice by her physicians. A cochlear implant was advisable, but a potential complication of the surgery was the loss of Ann's remaining hearing. Lin opted to avoid the risk and had Ann wear hearing aids instead. The disability was a trial for both parents and child. The family lived by the ocean back then. Such was the moisture level that Ann would not infrequently contract respiratory illnesses. Unable to express herself, she would end up either banging her head against a wall or clawing her parents' arms, legs, or faces with her finger nails when she felt sick. If particularly irritated, she would resort to biting right into their flesh.

* * *

Jeh heard about a 'Mrs. Cheng' from the National Women's League;

she was described as a foreign woman who taught deaf children to talk. Jeh made the call and the voice on the other line responded in fluent Taiwanese, catching Jeh completely off guard. Joanna was, as ever, more than happy to be Ann's auditory-verbal therapist.

Because the two families lived quite close to each other, Jeh usually took Ann to Joanna's house for the sessions. Joanna used materials she used on Alana, and made the house itself a study aid by referring to objects in the living room, dining room, and even the fishpond. Jeh recalled for me one class in which Joanna demonstrated to Ann the art of cake baking. From the ingredients and the recipe to the taste and whom to invite over to share it, it was a bountiful source of topics for conversation between teacher and pupil. Joanna had a naturalistic approach to cultivating Ann's communication, she would be reactive in conversation, looking to pursue points of discussion that Ann showed an interest in. Her aptitude for eliciting responses from Ann impressed Jeh.

In the time Joanna was Ann's therapist, the Children's Hearing Foundation was established. Joanna's time became in greater and greater demand, so a substitute was found for Ann. Ann continued at the Foundation until the beginning of elementary school. When her course of years at the Foundation was completed, Ann had yet to master spoken language, and thus it fell to her mother to continue therapy with her. A tutor was hired to assist Ann in her schoolwork. The learning journey through which parents must lead their deaf children is long and arduous, and not one simply of acquiring language. Social skills need nurturing, and deaf children must develop the mental toughness to deal with a world that does and will continue to discriminate against their disability. The way children respond to the trials the world heaps on them can be less than productive if guidance is not forthcoming. Jeh visited Ann's preschool and elementary schools to forewarn her teachers of Ann's condition. She urged Ann's classmates to talk to Ann as much as possible, for the benefit of her hearing and speech. Jeh would on occasion observe her daughter in class, following her at school for an entire month after she commenced first grade. She of course realized that, she had to learn to allow Ann her independence. Having done everything within her power to build up a solid foundation for her daughter, she let Ann to explore the world herself. There are limits to the help parents can offer, beyond which their efforts become a hindrance.

* * *

Lin was restricted in the assistance he could provide Ann, owing to his own disability. Nonetheless, artistic expression, as with the wider world, was a medium by which he could communicate with his daughter. It was especially fortuitous, that when his daughter entered elementary school and began art classes, it became apparent she had inherited her father's gifts and creative spark. Jeh showed me Ann's paintings: one of them titled 'Having hot pot' and the other 'Diving'. Her canvasses were filled with a multitude of colors, evincing the vibrancy of her own talents. Ann had learnt sign language to help her communicate with her dad. Discussions of art between them are invariably accompanied by a wild failing of hands, to the point where even Ann's sister complains, 'they are so noisy'!

Lin had, at the time of her birth, felt defeated by Ann's deafness. Recollecting the hardship he experienced in his own life, he had feared she would face the same. Thankfully, in our time, a hearing impairment is not a consignment to a life of silence and speechlessness. Ann talks and plays music, on both piano and flute. And paints. In addition, she expresses herself in such a myriad ways that it fills her father with pride. Indeed, with his own artistic training and accomplishments, he is his daughter's best mentor.

Lin even taught Ann English. Jeh chuckled when I asked her how; she has no clue. It is a secret shared between them. Now a teenage girl, and despite her expressive prowess, Ann prefers to remain demure. Out with her father, she is not averse to telling him to shush if he attracts unwanted attention with his signing. Low key is the maxim she lives by.

* * *

Lin loves to communicate. Every time we stopped at a red light, he immediately took out a piece of paper to write notes to his passengers. He tells anecdotes of his apparent car-racing days. To make sure he was convincing enough, he uses pictures as evidence. These conversations were so protracted the cars behind would blow their horns out of impatience. The earnest with which he shares his thoughts with the world could not be denied. Self-expression is perhaps that part of our nature that makes us definitively human. It is something to which we are all entitled. That all might hear, and none go unheard: such has been the hope behind Joanna's devotion and the work of the Children's Hearing Foundation.

Chapter 12

Angel Mommy

Pain in life is inescapable. That she looked beyond her own pain, to the suffering of others, is what made Joanna's life so remarkable.

Christmas in Australia is a world away from the frosty weather of the northern hemisphere. December marks the beginning of the long Australian summer. Joanna spent December 2000 positively bathing in it, giving her pause to reflect on the abundance of her life. She had traversed half the globe to marry the man she loved; he had helped her raise two beautiful daughters. Soaking in the radiance of the southern hemisphere's sun and surrounded by her family, Joanna thought of how blessed she was to have spent so many Christmases in company with love, and none more than this, the final Christmas of her life.

It had been over a year since the news came. In September 1999, on the other end of the earth, the air was infused with the smell of autumn. Kenny Cheng was on a business trip to Mainland China when he received a call from his wife in Taipei. During a routine medical check-up, a tumor, likely malignant, had been discovered in her breast. It hit Kenny hard and numb that it could happen to one such as Joanna, to whom he was closer to than no one else. It was an impossibility. Away from her and alone, Kenny could not sleep that night, but instead lay awake, crying in the darkness.

He was eager to fly back home the next day to see Joanna. They were ready to fight the disease together; they didn't want to waste one second, but first Joanna thought she ought to gain an understanding of what she was fighting. She and Kenny consulted several doctors at the Veteran's Hospital where she was diagnosed. Her good friend also referred her to other well-known doctors in the field.

She also took counsel from her parents. Their view on the matter was somewhat different from the physicians Joanna had consulted. They were dismissive of conventional medicine, and recommended Joanna undergo alternative treatment. Joanna chose to follow her family's advice. She flew to Tucson, and began a course of vitamins, a special diet, Chinese herbal medicine and acupuncture, among other things. It was the opinion of the practitioners caring for her that in this way, there was a 70 percent chance she would be cured of her cancer.

Joanna was an admirable fighter. She followed her doctors' every prescription, without fuss or complaint. However, three months passed with only a deterioration of her condition. The alternative specialists suggested she relocated to a German clinic, which she followed. Once again, she simply became worse. Joanna returned to Taiwan, and began chemotherapy. Six months thus elapsed between detection of the cancer and the commencement of the conventional intervention originally advocated. And, in contrast to the treatment she had previously undergone, its impact was veritably instantaneous.

Just as with Alana, her hearing impairment and the Foundation, Joanna was spurred to altruism by this new personal crisis. She involved herself in the promotion of breast cancer awareness among Taiwanese women. On August 19, 2000, she participated in the launch of two mobile women's testing centers, buses which would tour the country, making it easier for women to have their breasts checked. When interviewed by the press at the event, Joanna did not hide the fact that there were moments when she felt weak and hopeless. 'When I learnt I had cancer, my immediate reaction was "where can I run to escape this thing?" But you can't run. You have to face it head on.'

The experience led Joanna to a reevaluation of her whole life. She slowed her pace and spent more time with her family, and herself. 'Every day is a bonus for me; it is a gift from God,' she said. But being Joanna, she could not come to a complete halt. She still busied herself with the activities of the Foundation. Her latest initiative was a campaign agitating for the government to take over of the pre-school education of hearing-impaired children. Joanna remarked that one could can only taste the sweetness of helping others through one's own suffering, and the more she was put through, the more she was motivated to push herself.

By November 2000, Joanna's chemotherapy had become near to ineffective. The disease was eating her physical being away. Kenny remembers how Joanna sought inner peace through meditation when she suffered the worst physically. She felt wrapped in love. Lying in bed, Joanna was at ease though she knew her life had reached its end. Joanna's countenance was in no way depressed. Her face showed purity and beauty. She had only worldly concern, for Joy and Alana. It grieved her that she would not see them grow up.

In May 2001, Joanna entered the next, stronger, harsher phase in chemotherapy treatment. It was at this time that her condition worsened dramatically: cancer cells were detected spreading to her brain. She was transferred to an intensive unit. In the evening of May 28, she slipped into a coma. Shortly after, she was pronounced brain dead. Kenny tried to contain his sadness, whispering into his wife's ear that he would take good care of their daughters. He wanted her to leave this world content. Her life support was disengaged a week or so later. She passed away; only forty-seven years old.

Her life began and concluded with love. Joanna has said farewell to this world, but the love and compassion she left behind will continue to serve the deaf of Taiwan. Life must end. Love may last forever.

Chapter 13

Pass Down the Torch

Joanna's spirit and mission has stayed on long after her body passed away. In the final months of her life, she did not allow herself to be overwhelmed by grief. She held on tight to the Foundation and the teachers, urging them to 'keep the fire burning'...

On January 5, 2002, a reunion of sorts, hosted by the Foundation, took place in the media room of Eslite Bookstore in Taipei. More than one hundred deaf children and their families filled the small space. On the stage, there was a picture of Joanna, smiling her usual bright-as-sunshine smile. It was as if she never left.

A choir of cherubim, angelic figures, walked onto the stage; each one of them had a hearing deficit. They were dressed in white robes, had rings of light on their heads, and a pair of wings on their backs. They looked excited and yet shy. One by one, they said hello to the audience and introduced themselves. Then, in full chorus, they sang 'Twinkle Twinkle Little Star'. The parents and teachers listened with full attention. A passerby might have been heard to say that the singing was far from perfect, but to its intended audience, it sounded heaven sent. It was a milestone moment for many of their parents. It was a tribute to all they had endured to raise their children in a world of sound. Their speech may not have been the finest, but at least they were able to communicate, learn and continue their journey in life with confidence.

In attendance at the event was Dinah Hu, Chief of Staff at the

Foundation's Taipei Centre. She marveled at the performance and at what the Foundation had accomplished since its establishment. These children owed their quality of life to it, and Joanna's visionary leadership.

Dinah, a first-generation Foundation teacher, had once flown high with the corporate flock. However, despite its material rewards, she found that life emotionally unfulfilling. Therefore, when she read the Foundation's job advertisements in the papers, she decided it was time for a change of direction. She did not have any relevant qualifications, experience, or education, only the passion to teach. Therefore, from the beginning, Dinah was far from optimistic about her recruitment prospects. During the interview process, she was impressed by Joanna's character and sincerity. Joanna described to her in detail how she helped her own deaf daughter to learn to speak, and her determination to promote auditory-verbal therapy in Taiwan. Joanna regarded the only prerequisites for employment at her new organization to be, first, love for children and, second, a willingness to do everything within one's power to help them. This was at a time when the Foundation lacked even the basic rudiments of an educational institution. Indeed, it was nothing more than an idea. Dinah confesses she entertained her doubts about the legitimacy of the operation, but she leapt aboard nevertheless, on the strength of Joanna's conviction.

Second-generation Foundation teachers had similar experiences. Lillian was a secretary and one time substitute teacher. Her interest in education had been lifelong, and, as a change from the ordinary, she decided to pursue a career at the Foundation. Her interview went well, but when the offer of a position was extended to her, she met it hesitantly. It took Joanna some three hours of discussion to persuade her to accept it. Joanna took personal responsibility for hiring every teacher at the Foundation. Amy Chen, a former teacher at a mainstream elementary school, came to the Foundation because of her frustration at the way deaf education was handled at her school. Special education had always fascinated her, and the Foundation offered an opportunity to explore that fascination. As with Lillian, hesitation struck Amy when it came time to step onboard. Her parents particularly were averse to a career move, fearing that, were she to leave her job, she would be unable to return if either she failed to secure a position at the Foundation or the organization itself were to fold. But again, the power of Joanna's charisma gave Amy, like Lillian, the confidence to take the risk.

Because of the personal role Joanna took in managing her staff, each teacher at the Foundation who knew her had a special affection for Joanna. They all thought themselves Joanna's favorite. Indeed it was a source of amusement. Foundation staff missed Joanna most of all, because of being Joanna's favorite. Amy, among the group, interjected that it was her understanding she was Joanna's favorite. Then the remaining teachers began bickering that they each were Joanna's true favorite. It was a testament to Joanna's loving style of leadership.

At CHF, there are several scenario rooms, individually designed to look like a living room, dining room, and bedrooms. The intention is to make it easier for the parents to apply classroom teaching in everyday life. Teachers prepare the content of therapy based on the condition and learning goal of each student. To the uniformed, there may seem to be no rhyme or reason to the games therapist play with their students. But every one of them has been painstakingly engineered towards a specific therapeutic purpose.

For example, when a teacher initiates how to pronounce 'ah', a model airplane may be used. This familiarizes the children with the sound of airplane passing by. Alternatively, a doll may be used to teach the compound sound 'wu-ah', to approximate in written English the phonetics of Mandarin. The key point is to repeat these inputs. Again, to familiarize the students with the pronunciation of the word doll, the teacher would repeat patiently, 'one doll for you, one doll for mommy, and one doll for me. So how many dolls are there in total?' In this way, children are simultaneously taught the sounds that comprise the word and the correct usage of the word itself.

Lessons must be appropriate for the student. The oldest student at the Foundation is a 30-year-old businessman, and his lessons are tailored to suit him individually, just as every other student. This is somewhat of a departure from the normal course at other educational institutions, whether elementary or university level, where syllabi and class content are standardized for batches of pupils. Amy had been a substitute teacher at an elementary school, heading a large class of students, and was unprepared for the rigors of designing lesson plans for individuals when she began at the Foundation. She had to be far more responsive to the needs of her students and their parents.

Besides classes tailor-made by the Foundation, parents of Foundation students are expected themselves to design activities and games using resources on hand at home. For example, taking pictures of a child's daily life and making them a sequence of photo cards can help reinforce new words in child's vocabulary.

Lillian remarked, 'on the difference between the outstanding and the average students at the Foundation, there is only one reason: the time, effort and heart parents put into educating their children.'

* * *

Often, it takes all of a therapist's skill simply to get their wards to sit down and pay attention. There used to be a student who would start crying as soon as he entered the classroom and not stop until his session was over. His mother put herself through much rigmarole to get him to keep quiet. It was by ignoring his tears that she and his therapist managed to teach him better. They would leave him alone in the therapy room, to give him the impression he had been abandoned there. He would cry and cry, but eventually discover that it had no effect whatsoever on his situation. Teachers at the Foundation are almost as much behavioral therapists as linguistic ones. A responsibility demands patience. No scolding, no spanking, and no snatching: these are rules by which all therapists must abide, and it is at times a challenge to do so. Lillian can recount times when, because her students have been more focused on the accoutrements of the classroom, rather than the lessons, she has forcefully grabbed things from their hands out of frustration. She knows, however, that she must act as a model to be emulated by the children, for they would learn from her behavior. Children learn from the adults around them. Abrupt physicality might solve the problems confronting the moment, but it will leave an undesirable mark on the child's mind.

Saturday afternoon is usually the busiest time for the Foundation, popular among parents as the most convenient time to arrange therapy sessions. From the observation rooms, looking in on the classrooms from the one-way mirror, you can see moms or dads with their children, or both parents with their kids. Grandma or grandpa may even be found in tow. Each family has its own story going on inside the classroom. In one room was a mother, looking very young with a leopard print coat, red highlight in her hair, and heavy make-up, in the company of a much younger girl. A man sat next to the two of them, presumably the father, nonchalance expressed by every angle of his demeanor. The therapist wondered to herself whether the couple had recently fought in a domestic quarrel. It is not unknown for parents to fight right in the class, typically over who is more to blame for a child's lack of improvement. In such circumstances, teachers are called upon to intervene, settle the dispute and return sanity to their classrooms. Far more frequently, however, the goodwill of parents and teachers encourages close friendships between the two parties. Parents often keep in touch with former teachers well after the time of their child at the Foundation has reached an end.

Therapists can find themselves acting as parents to the parents. In one case where a parent refused to accept that her hearing-impaired child had attention deficit disorder. She was obstinate to accept her son's physician's prescriptions that her son take medication to overcome the condition. The boy's therapist took on the task of counseling his mother, to help her mature to the realities.

* * *

During her life, Joanna was a lighthouse, guiding ships lost on the vast expanse of a dark, otherwise un-navigable sea. She managed the administration of the Foundation, and had sole responsibility for fundraising. She personally helped promote its work, to the point of dropping by the homes of the families of potential and actual clients. She was the tabernacle housing the Foundation's soul. Its staff recalls, vividly, that even in the last few months of her life, consigned as she was to her bed, she still bore her light ahead of them.

The life of the Foundation's now fell into Kenny's hands. Joanna had a philanthropist's personality. Kenny has brought his entrepreneurial outlook to the Foundation. The Foundation is an organic organization, which has matured and developed through time. It must, like any organism, adapt to its environment if it is to flourish. Joanna's departure was a test to the Foundation's existence, but it also marked the beginning of a transformation. Metamorphosis can be violent. In March and April in 2001, Foundation experimented with charging a fee for its service, turning many parents away. Several rounds of internal discussion concluded with the decision to revert to a voluntary donation system, which allowed parents to give to the Foundation as much as according to their willingness and financial means. Kenny's vision is for this system to become a viable, sustainable and sole source of income for the foundation, such that it is loosened from its dependence on institutional and business benefactors.

Dr. Dai-Shen Seetoo, Senior Professor at the National Chengchi University, has commented that what distinguishes the Foundation as a not-for-profit organization is its acutely honed expertise in the field in which it operates. It needs to promote the merits of a localized auditory-verbal methodology, the sum of the knowledge and effort of many professionals, to the Chinese-speaking world. With CHF's limited amount of resources, to do so it must in turn, according to Si-To, evolve from a service centre to a training centre. That is, it must move from offering therapy directly to its clients, to accrediting therapists from other institutions. This approach will maximize the use of the Foundation's resources and expertise. And in that vein, starting from 2001, the Foundation's entered into a partnership with the Fu-Dan Hospital in Shanghai, stationing attachés there to share Taiwanese know-how with the Mainland.

The 2002 reunion saw the Foundation staff design a statue of a little mermaid. They drew upon a child's story, wherein a deaf, mute mermaid longs for the day when she learns to speak and express her love. Children attending classes at the Foundation desire, in the same way, to express their love for their parents, teachers and friends. And, for those who remember her, Joanna. She dared to do the seemingly impossible, to see to it that within twenty years every deaf child in Taiwan would be able to speak. She dared without hesitation; she dared to devote herself passionately to that dream.

Chapter 14

The Legacy and The Steps into the Future

The Foundation keeps Joanna's office as it was before, as if she were still there, protecting the organization. But since her passing, the Foundation has been through much change.

2005, and another Christmas holiday was approaching. Fifteen hearing-impaired children were on a visit to Song-Yuan nursing home in Taipei, to send messages of love to the resident senior citizens. Sprightly and spiritedly, they sang "Silent Night". The senior citizens listened intently; the song was perfectly evocative of a beautiful, snow laden Christmas eve. Different in tone but no less engaging, the children next sang 'Where did the Snowman go', and 'Frolicking, rollicking ditty'. Before undergoing auditory-verbal therapy, these children had only most modest hearing, and no speech whatsoever. Now they were singing and sharing the childish glee with others.

* * *

In late 2005, The Foundation was just as warm as before. Therapy rooms were busy with teachers and students, and the hallways were alive with rambunctious kids and their not-a-little vexed parents. Joanna's old office had, and will continue to be, kept in the state it was when she passed away, as a memorial to her. Pictures with her beautiful smiles filled the room, as if she never left it. This room remained unchanged, but the remainder of the Foundation was quite a bit different, and in such a way as would have no doubt filled Joanna with pride.

* * *

The Foundation was Joanna's third child, and it was Kenny's pledge to look after it in her absence. Taking over from his wife, Kenny has made many innovations to ensure the longevity of the Foundation's operations, and spread its influence so that it can serve the needs of Mandarin speakers beyond Taiwan. He has brought his business acumen to the role, and has begun instituting modern management practices in the way the Foundation is run, something he hopes may be an example for other Taiwanese charities.

Kenny is of the view that it is the human element that is most critical to further promotion and exploitation of the potential of auditory-verbal therapy, the therapists themselves. The Foundation has begun collaborating with Taiwan's universities to run accreditation programs for prospective teachers of the deaf. The first of these efforts was a series of eight courses at the Special-Education Department of Chung-Yuan Christian University. The Foundation has also played a part of an initiative to establish a Hearing Department with MacKay Medical School, and collaborating with Chang-Gung University to establish a graduate program focusing on the early treatment of hearing impairment. These modes of cooperation help not only cultivate the talents of new therapist, but also provide a formal mode of further study for the Foundation's existing staff. The next frontier Kenny sees is the provision of master-level courses in auditory-verbal therapy in Taiwan.

In addition to new accreditation programs, Kenny is driving innovation in the way professional knowledge is shared. He is pushing for greater use of information technology in therapy. The Foundation has at is disposal a 'Knowledge Centre', an information system that integrates data on teaching methods, student evaluation and consultation. This enables teachers at different locations or points of time to exchange their perspectives and experiences, thereby continuously improving the efficiency and quality of their practice.

For example, when practitioners encounter more complicated students, say a child with multiple disabilities, they can access records of similar cases. The records may include teaching methods and reference books. Instantly, therapists have access to the accumulated wisdom of their colleagues.

The system also includes a database tracking the Foundation's benefactors, a great aid to its fundraising efforts. The primary income source of non-profit organizations like the Foundation is gratuitous giving. Therefore, it should be the top priority of these organizations to maximize the effect of each penny donated. Kenny is keen on importing the efficiency ethic of for-profit business to Foundation administrators.

* * *

The Foundation's current management team is led by J Yeh. A graduate in human resources, she was the manager of Wonderland's human resource department. In pursuit of Kenny's goal to improve the efficiency of the Foundation's workings, she has been responsible for heading an organizational revolution at the Foundation. Changes have been made to staffing, compensation, and teachers' working hours. Yeh admits these adjustments are quite significant, but she justifies them by asking her staff to put themselves in the shoes of their benefactors, who would demand their money be used as effectively as possible.

Technological advances have meant that hearing impairment is being detected in more children, earlier in their lives than ever before. Yeh foresees a corresponding increase in demand for the Foundation's service. For newly diagnosed hearing-impaired children, much assessment is needed, assessment beginning from the time when parents first contact the Foundation to the time their therapy commences. Questions like the following have to be answered first. Is the Foundation the most appropriate provider of therapy for the child? What is the child's hearing and learning potential? Are there multiple disabilities involved? How committed are the child's parents to fight what will inevitably be a long battle? In the past, answering these questions was a matter of the evaluator's personal judgment. Now, Yeh requires social workers to establish a set of evaluation indexes that include subjective and objective items. This not only saves time, but also provides results that are more reliable.

"I never thought I could be so aggressive working in a non-profit organization", said J of her career change. It is not all a ruthless push to maximize efficiency, her experience at the Foundation have a softer side to them. In her work she sees many parents devote themselves to coming to classes with their children, to the point of putting their careers on hold to help their children learn to hear and speak. This kind of selfless devotion is the source of Yeh's satisfaction in her role at the Foundation.

* * *

To date, the Foundation has seen five generations of internally trained teachers. With a major in industrial design, Candy Chang was one of the special cases. While studying in Taichung City, she worked part time in a local city office. Because of a hearing-impaired co-worker, she was introduced to Sound Home Hearing and Learning Center, where she later became a volunteer worker.

Sound Home recommended she attend a training session for volunteer workers hosted by the Labor Bureau. It entailed her coming up to Taipei two days a week for six months. She then worked for the Taipei branch of Sound Home as a project leader, working with United Way Taiwan. She thereby brought herself in contact with the social workers at the Foundation. At the time, the Foundation was conducting its fifth round of therapist recruitment. Candy had an interest in the Foundation's work, but by the time she heard of the intake, there were only five days left in which she could make an application. She rushed it, but fortunately, was successful, and was offered a position at the Taipei office.

Working with children was something new to Candy, which she found to be the starkest difference between the Foundation and Sound Home. Kids can be shy and reluctant to participate in therapy. One has to ease them into it. Candy discovered that the most effective way to warm children to therapy was to be more childlike she. Playfulness is the essence of childhood. If a therapist is able to introduce herself as her student's playmate, she stands a better chance of being an effective teacher.

At the Foundation, Candy felt as if she was part of a big family. The senior teachers are very willing to share their experiences. Even with two years of experiences under her belt, Candy can see much still needs to be learnt in the field. She is currently pursuing her interest in advanced study of child psychology, linguistic therapy, and behavior management.

* * *

Alana, the little girl whom Joanna devoted so much time and energy to, is now a beautiful 16-year-old young woman. As her father, Kenny observed Alana's development closely. He found that, her eloquence aside, she still needs a lot of help going forward. These observations made Kenny think about the many children who graduated from the Foundation over the years. Do their parents realize that graduation is not the end, and that their kids may digress if the treatment of their deafness is not regarded as a lifelong process? Joanna was determined to help others because she saw how greatly Alana benefited from auditory-verbal therapy. Kenny saw in Alana the need for continuous care of the hearing-impaired. Across the leadership of the two, the core of the Foundation's agenda has remained the same: to provide more deaf children with long-term assistance, helping them live to their fullest potential in the audible world.

Appendix I

From Sadness to Strength

June 2002

Joanna has left us for more than one year. This book begins with her and ends with her.

In the last year, I, as her partner for life, felt nostalgic missing her and felt determined to take over the responsibility of the Foundation. All kinds of emotions rushed in whenever I look back to the years I spent with Joanna. I always say that Joanna is the most selfless person I have ever met. To me, this is more of something I'd like to learn than just a compliment.

I think her selflessness came from two characters. First of them is generosity, and the other is sensitivity. It might have been the way she grew up that instilled a sweet energy in her that made her embrace every thing with an open mind and unlimited passion. She was also willing to make a positive change on the less-than-perfect things in life. However, she never ignored others' feelings while she lived the fullest of her life. On the contrary, she was sensitive to the needs of each one around her, who always felt how warm and caring she was.

Being generous and sensitive, Joanna enriched my life and left a selfless legacy behind, Children's Hearing Foundation. However, only in the last year, after knowing her for twenty years, I regret that I did not take in every trace of her wonderful character onto myself. In the past, she complemented my calmness with her passion and my logical thinking with her emotional approach. It is not easy to face everything on my own, but I believe I will carry on.

But how? That has been the core subject of my self-evaluation in the last year. Because of Joanna's charisma and the mission rooted deep inside of us, the Foundation tended to be more low profile and conservative. Although lots of efforts was put in the operation of the Foundation, it was not well known by society. After Joanna passed away, I started contemplating if our personal efforts and support from our business could sustain CHF and even expand its service. I believe the answer is no. Neither people nor businesses will last forever. In addition, there are environmental risks involved. Once individuals or single businesses can no longer afford to give to a non-profit organization, would the whole society have to give up on a dream based on a greater purpose?

Therefore, I think it is necessary to make adjustments to CHF's operational strategy. First, we should strive to expand the scope of involvement. CHF used to depend on donations of a few parties. Such a fund-raising model certainly faced the challenge of environmental risks as mentioned earlier. Expanding the sources of funding will help diversify the risks. From my perspective, under this initiative, there are two approaches: firstly, increase the number of long-term small-amount donations from the public. This helps CHF to acquire the needed resources from those who relate to its vision and mission and give small donations, but on a regular basis. CHF will be responsible for informing every donor of its work process and result. And no doubt, a good communication channel between the foundation and the general public needs to be in place, which helps potential donors become aware of CHF's goals and willing to support them with action.

Secondly, develop partnerships with related government agencies. This requires integration of resources among the organizations involved and joint management of social welfare service. The fact that CHF and the Yi-Lan county government jointly opened a hearing training center in October 2001 served as one of the best examples of this model. The government provided the infrastructure and other resources required for teaching, while CHF was responsible for the expertise and teachers in AVT. The partnership brought opportunities for the deaf children in Yi-Lan to benefit from the education in their hometown. We hope this is not a stand-alone case, and will continue to introduce this model to Taipei city, Kao-Hsiung City, and other places outside of Yi-Lan, so children in other regions can also learn to speak with possible minimum costs.

However, there was another key factor in making a professional non-profit organization sustainable: continue strengthening its core competency. For CHF, the core is undoubtedly AVT. We have described in this book the long and challenging process to localize this methodology, which helps children with severe hearing deficit learn to speak. What is so precious about the application of this therapy in Chinese-speaking countries is that it is a collection of efforts and knowledge of the teachers at CHF. Briefly, this therapy is the only local expertise in Chinese in the world. After reaching this milestone, we now begin to standardize this Chinese AVT as the next step. Two years ago, the staff at CHF started to "externalize" the methodology to create standard teaching material, and develop teaching principles and textbooks. We started sharing the knowledge by training internal and external teachers. At this time, we not only trained a group of new teachers for CHF, but also the first group of AVT teachers in Mainland China for Fu-Tan University in Shanghai.

I believe all these initiatives were only the beginning of upgrading CHF's core competency. We have to have high expectations for the foundation and keep improving ourselves. We expect CHF to continue growing in Taiwan to service more individuals and families, and eventually more countries. We hope to realize the goal of making a

CHF resource center for AVT in every Mandarin speaking region.

We have many people to thank for making CHF where it is today. I hope, at the one-year anniversary of Joanna's passing, this book records the footprints of Joanna and every one who worked with her at CHF, and shares her story with others. It is impossible to express my gratitude to all of you, but allow me, on behalf of Joanna, to say "thank you" to each one who has helped us along the way. I also hope, after reading this book, you can help us carry on with strength and work toward the realization of our goal: "In twenty years, every deaf child in Taiwan will be able to speak."

Kenny Cheng

Appendix II

Joanna's Last Letter to Her Daughters

Dear Bright and Alana,

I love you both so very, very much. I feel extremely lucky that we have shared so much love in this life. God is good to give us each other.

No matter what happens with my illness, I want to share some things with you two:

There is a bigger picture to life than just the material and physical things we deal with daily. In fact, our purpose is to realize that we are much more than the physical that we are spiritual beings that live forever. I believe I chose to try to realize this during this lifetime, and my Godself knew what experiences I need to make this possible. Each "challenge" pushes me to focus more and to be more real and honest with myself and God, more pure. I can feel that, and I can feel that without the push, I wouldn't know how to focus more. Of course, I wish everything could be easy and fun and I believe that once we know the Truth of who we are, all our worries and troubles are gone. In the meantime, I just take each day at a time. God has given me the strength to handle everything so far, and I trust He will continue to do so. It really helps to handle everything so far, and I trust He will continue to do so. It really helps to have this belief, and I do feel God's love for me and His certainty that everything is happening for my good (as hard as it seems on the outside!).

I write these things so that you, too, can focus as early as possible on the true goal of life. The best way is to think of God's love, and to become that love, so that you are one with God. Love for all is the key. You need not show on the outside that you love people; feeling it on the inside is enough. It will show itself in your actions, naturally.

Maintain faith in God no matter what. Pray all the time, and work toward knowing in your heart that God and you are the same.

The main thing, though, is that you know the depth of my love for you. I will do anything for you. My love for Daddy is the same.

Always listen to your inner voice. Do not let friends convince you of something you feel is not right. Your inner voice will tell you what to do. If you have a doubt, ask yourself quietly what to do, and listen for the answer.

There is a lot I could say, but the main thing is to let you know that I love you very much, and my love will always be with you!

Love,

Your mom, Joanna

Appendix III

Knowledge Center Structure of Children's Hearing Foundation

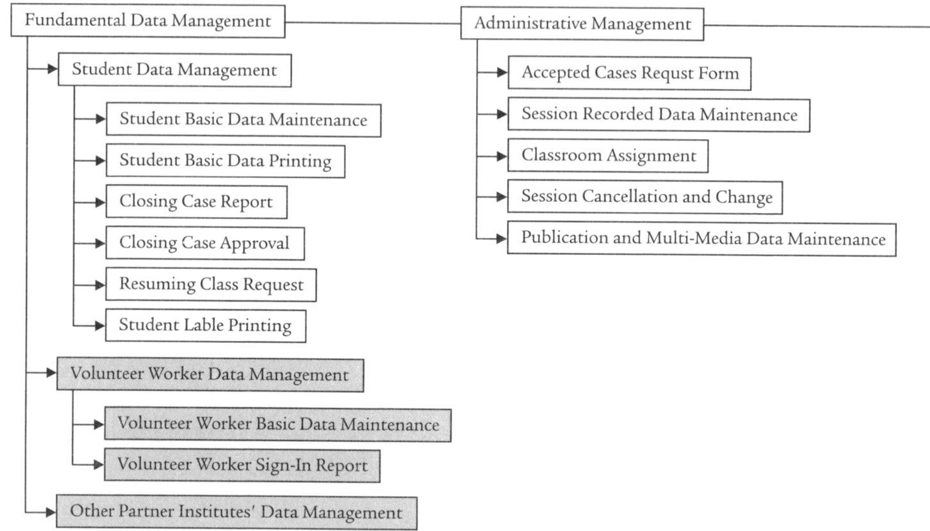

Note:

Items highlighted in grey were still under construction as of October 2007.

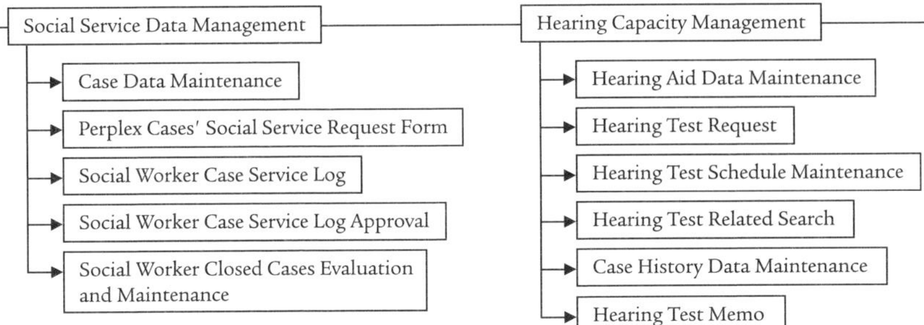
Social Service Data Management
Case Data Maintenance
Perplex Cases' Social Service Request Form
Social Worker Case Service Log
Social Worker Case Service Log Approval
Social Worker Closed Cases Evaluation and Maintenance
Hearing Capacity Management
Hearing Aid Data Maintenance
Hearing Test Request
Hearing Test Schedule Maintenance
Hearing Test Related Search
Case History Data Maintenance
Hearing Test Memo

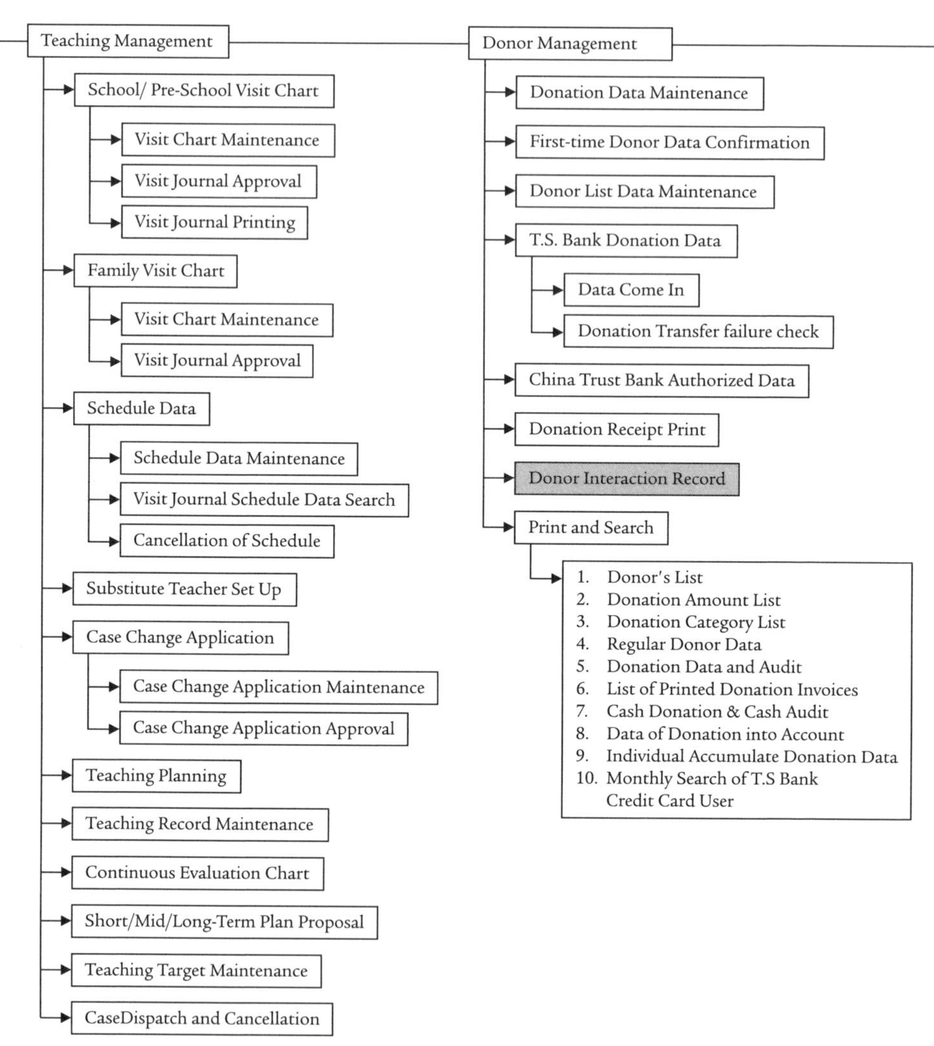
Teaching Management
School/ Pre-School Visit Chart
Visit Chart Maintenance
Visit Journal Approval
Visit Journal Printing
Family Visit Chart
Visit Chart Maintenance
Visit Journal Approval
Schedule Data
Schedule Data Maintenance
Visit Journal Schedule Data Search
Cancellation of Schedule
Substitute Teacher Set Up
Case Change Application
Case Change Application Maintenance
Case Change Application Approval
Teaching Planning
Teaching Record Maintenance
Continuous Evaluation Chart
Short/Mid/Long-Term Plan Proposal
Teaching Target Maintenance
CaseDispatch and Cancellation
Donor Management
Donation Data Maintenance
First-time Donor Data Confirmation
Donor List Data Maintenance
T.S. Bank Donation Data
Data Come In
Donation Transfer failure check
China Trust Bank Authorized Data
Donation Receipt Print
Donor Interaction Record
Print and Search
1. Donor's List
2. Donation Amount List
3. Donation Category List
4. Regular Donor Data
5. Donation Data and Audit
6. List of Printed Donation Invoices
7. Cash Donation & Cash Audit
8. Data of Donation into Account
9. Individual Accumulate Donation Data
10. Monthly Search of T.S Bank
Credit Card User

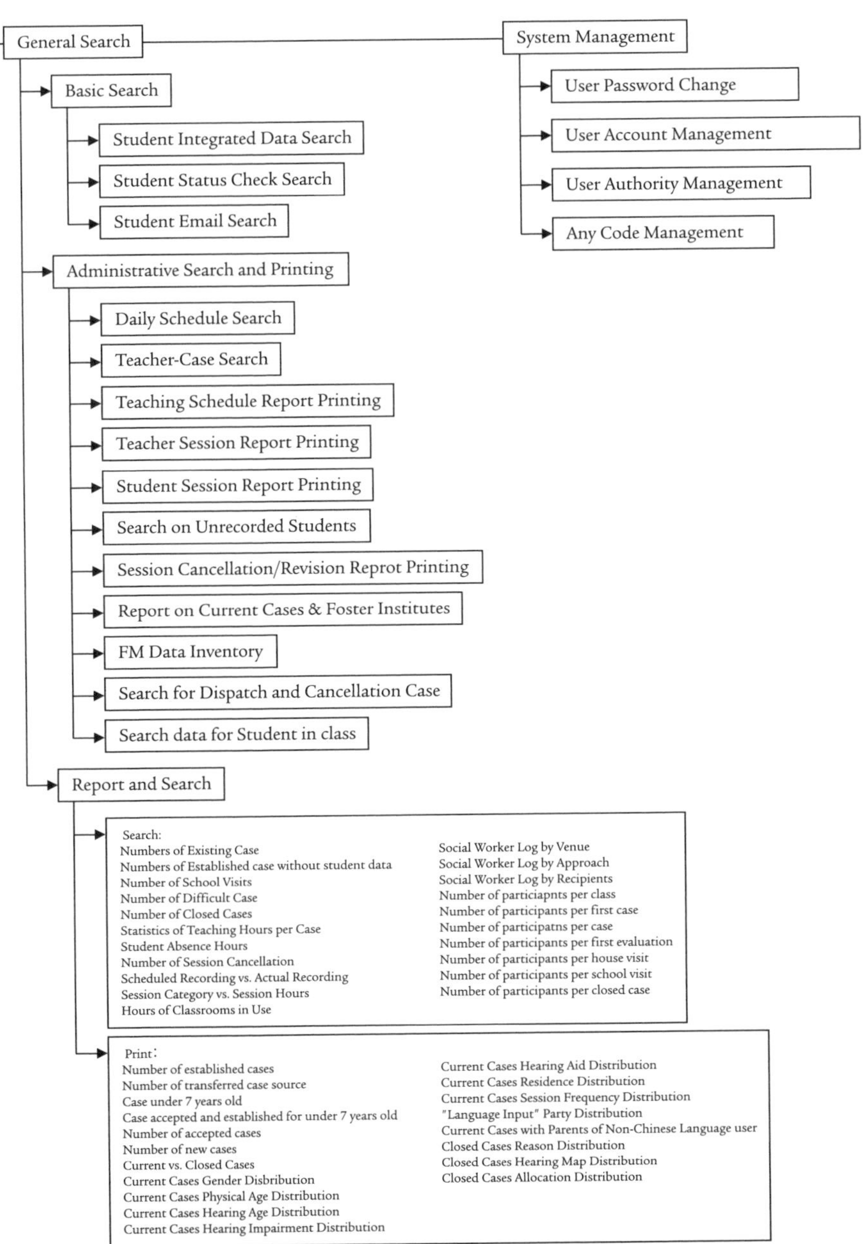
General Search
System Management
User Password Change
User Account Management
User Authority Management
Any Code Management
Basic Search
Student Integrated Data Search
Student Status Check Search
Student Email Search
Administrative Search and Printing
Daily Schedule Search
Teacher-Case Search
Teaching Schedule Report Printing
Teacher Session Report Printing
Student Session Report Printing
Search on Unrecorded Students
Session Cancellation/Revision Reprot Printing
Report on Current Cases & Foster Institutes
FM Data Inventory
Search for Dispatch and Cancellation Case
Search data for Student in class
Report and Search
Search:
Numbers of Existing Case
Numbers of Established case without student data
Number of School Visits
Number of Difficult Case
Number of Closed Cases
Statistics of Teaching Hours per Case
Student Absence Hours
Number of Session Cancellation
Scheduled Recording vs. Actual Recording
Session Category vs. Session Hours
Hours of Classrooms in Use
Social Worker Log by Venue
Social Worker Log by Approach
Social Worker Log by Recipients
Number of particiapnts per class
Number of participants per first case
Number of participatns per case
Number of participants per first evaluation
Number of participants per house visit
Number of participants per school visit
Number of participants per closed case
Print:
Number of established cases
Number of transferred case source
Case under 7 years old
Case accepted and established for under 7 years old
Number of accepted cases
Number of new cases
Current vs. Closed Cases
Current Cases Gender Disbribution
Current Cases Physical Age Distribution
Current Cases Hearing Age Distribution
Current Cases Hearing Impairment Distribution
Current Cases Hearing Aid Distribution
Current Cases Residence Distribution
Current Cases Session Frequency Distribution
"Language Input" Party Distribution
Current Cases with Parents of Non-Chinese Language user
Closed Cases Reason Distribution
Closed Cases Hearing Map Distribution
Closed Cases Allocation Distribution

Appendix IV

About Children's Hearing Foundation

The Children's Hearing Foundation (www.chfn.org.tw) is a not-for-profit organization dedicated to providing auditory-verbal therapy to the hearing-impaired children of Taiwan. The Foundation combines modern teaching methods with the latest technology in hearing aids and cochlear implants, to teach deaf children the skills they need to speak, go to regular schools, and live full, able-bodied lives in the hearing world.

Like its bifurcated name, the auditory-verbal methodology has two components. The first is audition. Uniquely, auditory-verbal therapy teaches by hearing, rather than lip reading, or sign language. In deed, the methodology emphasizes the exclusivity of audition as its only mode of teaching. The second component is verbal expression. Deaf children are taught to speak, to the exclusion of other modes of communication. The philosophy underpinning this approach is one that values integration: it says that the hearing-impaired ought, as far as possible, to integrate with the able-bodied community. Instrumentally, the best way of integrating the deaf into a hearing, speaking world is to teach them to hear and speak.

The Foundation's Services and activities include:

- Auditory-verbal therapy for hearing impaired children and their families.
- Audiology services, including regular hearing tests and hearing aid management using the latest equipment.
- A library with a collection of educational and children's

books for parents and professionals.

- Workshops for parents and professionals featuring many overseas and local speakers.
- Monthly parent meetings with educational speakers.
- Qualified social workers to help with family and financial problems.
- Infant screening in conjunction with affiliated hospitals. This is a pilot project to encourage universal infant hearing screening in Taiwan, with the goal that it one day be mandatory.

For more information, please contact us:

Children's Hearing Foundation
Taipei Headquarters
3F, No. 128, Yu Ming 6th Road, Taipei, Taiwan
Tel: 886-2-2827-4500
Fax: 886-2-2827-4555
Email: chfn@chfn.org.tw

Southern Taiwan Center
7F, No. 148, Chien-Chin Zone, Calvin-Cheng 4th Road, Kaohsiung, Taiwan
Tel: 886-7-215-0626
Fax: 886-7-216-1162
Email: chfnkhh@chfn.org.tw